Getting into MEDICINE

The essential guide to choosing a medical school and obtaining a place

DEDICATION

To my parents
A.R.H.

To Caroline
D.G.

Getting into MEDICINE

The essential guide to choosing a medical school and obtaining a place

Andrew R. Houghton

&

David Gray

Hodder & Stoughton

A MEMBER OF THE HODDER HEADLINE GROUP

The Authors

Dr Andrew R. Houghton, MA (Oxon.), BM, BCh, MRCP (UK),
is Specialist Registrar in Cardiology at Pilgrim Hospital,
Sibsey Road, Boston, Lincolnshire.

Dr David Gray, DM, MPH, BMedSci, BM, BS, MRCP (UK),
is Reader in Medicine & Honorary Consultant Physician at the
Department of Cardiovascular Medicine, University Hospital,
Queen's Medical Centre, Nottingham.

British Library Cataloguing in Publication Data

Houghton, Andrew
   Getting into medicine: the essential guide to choosing a
   medical school and obtaining a place
   1. Medical colleges – Great Britain   2. Medical colleges –
   Great Britain – Admission
   I. Title   II. Gray, David
   610.7'11'41

ISBN 0 340 70158 7

First published 1997
Impression number   10 9 8 7 6 5 4 3 2 1
Year   2002 2001 2000 1999 1998 1997

Printed in Great Britain for Hodder & Stoughton Educational, the educational publishing
division of Hodder Headline Plc, 338 Euston Road, London NW1 3BH, by Redwood Books,
Trowbridge.

Preface

There has never been a more exciting time to study medicine. Major changes in medical school curricula have taken place over the last few years, partly as a result of the General Medical Council's recommendations in *Tomorrow's Doctors*. Studying at medical school is now more varied, more interesting and more challenging than ever before.

Nonetheless, training to become a doctor should never be undertaken without a clear idea of what lies ahead. The rewards of a medical career must always be balanced against the very real demands it can make upon you.

In writing *Getting into Medicine*, we set out to provide the prospective medical school applicant with detailed information about every aspect of medical training. We hope that this book will give you some insight into what it takes to become a doctor. Our aim is not to persuade you to study medicine, but to help you to make your own decision. If you do decide upon a medical career, this book should also help you to achieve your ambitions.

Throughout the book, we have emphasised the importance of obtaining information from as many sources as possible. Too many people go into medicine with little idea about what is involved, and some end up feeling disillusioned as a result. We have practised what we preach by asking for hints and tips from current medical students, over 100 of which are included in the book as a result. Some of their quotations contradict one another, for which we make no apology. Everyone has a different view on what it is like to be a doctor – you should hear as many as possible and make up your *own* mind.

Andrew R. Houghton & David Gray

Acknowledgements

We would like to thank all of the medical schools and organisations that provided information for this book, and we are in particular indebted to Stuart Smith and the Department of Research and Statistics at UCAS for their help in the compilation of the admissions statistics.

Our thanks also go to the Education Committee of the General Medical Council for their permission to reproduce the principal recommendations from *Tomorrow's Doctors*.

We are grateful to all the students who found time to give us the quotations that we have included throughout the book, especially:

Nick Abbott	Jill Milner
Sharedah Adnan	Jonathan Nash
Matthijs Backx	Marios Nicolaou
Zumla Cader	Clare Pattenden
Christakis Christodoulou	Leeanne Ramdin
Katharine Gairdner	Anna Roslani
Claire Gibbin	Rachel Stevens
Lyndon Gommersall	Joanna Stokoe
Shameem Abdul Haque	Ian Stott
Katherine Keen	Mai Wakatsuki
Ourania Kolokotroni	Tom Walton
Stuart McCracken	Anna Williams
James McFetrich	Joanna Williams

We are also grateful to everyone who gave us suggestions and constructive criticism while we prepared *Getting into Medicine*, to our wives and families for their patience and to everyone at Hodder & Stoughton Educational for their guidance and support.

Contents

Preface   *v*

Acknowledgements   *vi*

1 **So you want to be a doctor?**   *1*
What it takes. Choosing your sixth-form options. Mature students.

2 **Choosing a medical school**   *8*
The medical course. *Tomorrow's Doctors*. No science A levels? Entry
requirements. Course emphasis. Location. Intercalated degrees.
Elective period. Length of course. Interview policy. What next?

3 **A guide to the UK medical schools**   *21*

4 **Applying via UCAS**   *76*
General points. Completing the UCAS form. After you have completed
the form. Interviews, offers and rejections.

5 **Interviews**   *86*
Preparing for your interview. At the interview. After the interview.
Receiving your grades. Back to square one?

6 **Preparing for medical school**   *106*
Accommodation. Money. The armed forces.

7 **The medical course**   *112*
The integrated medical course – what to expect. Vacations. Early
clinical experience. The clinical course. Student support. Studying
abroad.

8 **An intercalated degree**   *129*

9 **The elective period**   *133*

10 **Examinations**   *138*
Examinations in medical school. Types of examinations. What if you
fail an examination? Learning strategies. Postgraduate examinations.

11 **Housejobs**   *145*
Choosing your house officer posts. Preparation for your house officer
year. Starting work. Basic house officer duties. The end of your house
officer year.

12 A career in medicine 152
What influences career choice? Which career for you? Postgraduate training. Career preferences. Careers in medicine.

13 So is medicine for you? 164
What have you got from this book? Thinking of taking a year out? Maximising your chances of admission.

FURTHER READING & INFORMATION 169

Medical school. University application. Money matters.
The armed forces. Taking a year out. Mature students.
Overseas students. Studying in Scotland. Internet resources.

APPENDIX 1: *Tomorrow's Doctors* 175

APPENDIX 2: *Prospectus requests* 177

CHAPTER ONE

So you want to be a Doctor?

'Patients must be able to trust doctors with their lives and well-being. To justify that trust, we as a profession have a duty to maintain a good standard of practice and care and to show respect for human life.'

GUIDANCE FROM THE GENERAL MEDICAL COUNCIL

This book is for anyone who is thinking about studying to become a doctor and this, presumably, includes you. If so, we hope that you find it both informative and interesting. Our aims are three-fold:

- First, we describe what going to medical school and practising as a doctor *really* involve.
- Second, we detail the unique features of each of the United Kingdom's medical schools, to help you choose *where* to apply.
- Third, we tell you how to maximise your chances of obtaining a place.

We believe that medicine is one of the most rewarding careers on offer. However, despite our enthusiasm for medicine, we also recognise that it is often demanding and sometimes routine. We do not, therefore, intend to try and *persuade* you to apply to medical school. Instead, we want to help you to make up your *own* mind about whether medicine is the right career for you.

We cannot overemphasise the importance of obtaining as much information and hearing as many viewpoints as possible. We have included quotations from a diverse range of students at different stages in their medical training, but you should make an effort to speak to medical students and doctors yourself so that you can ask questions and hear their views first-hand.

'If you enjoy studying, memorising facts and doing a lot of reading, and if you have some idea of what you're in for (the pressure, the competition, the hours), and you're still interested, then medicine is for you!'

What it takes

To some, the price of admission to the medical profession may seem high. You must be prepared to:

- work steadily to get the right grades to get into medical school and take numerous examinations;
- work hard after graduation to gain experience and develop your confidence, knowledge and expertise;
- pass your postgraduate exams at the earliest opportunity;
- maintain throughout your working lifetime your obvious interest in science (especially medical science) and keep up to date with the latest developments;
- accept that at times you may need to take responsibility and make decisions (big ones) quickly and confidently, and live with the consequences;
- seek help from a colleague when you are at the limits of your knowledge and experience;
- learn to cope with critically-ill patients and the (sometimes unrealistic) expectations of relatives.

To get the best out of medicine you will need to master technological and scientific advances with a blend of enthusiasm and determination, but most of the time you will simply need basic skills and knowledge, perseverance, compassion and stamina in more or less equal doses. Most important of all, you must be prepared to listen to your patients and never leave them thinking that you could have done more for them.

This may seem a tall order. Perhaps you feel that just three years of study as an undergraduate should be enough to get you started on a career, that the responsibilities of a doctor are too great, that the stresses of coping with demanding patients are too much. Ask any doctor – the price is most certainly worth paying.

So far, we have concentrated solely on what efforts you will have to make to become a doctor. How can we explain what rewards await you as you seek to embark on the first step towards the medical profession?

It may be near-impossible for you as you battle with A levels, but imagine yourself in about seven or eight years' time. You have graduated from medical school with your hard-earned degrees and you have spent a little time in your first post as a junior doctor. The hours of study and the stresses of exams have paid off – medicine is at last making sense, you feel comfortable and, most important of all, you are enjoying yourself. You are on the first rung of the medical ladder, yet your seniors cannot fail to notice that your clinical skills are developing fast. You are beginning to *think* like a doctor.

The rewards come quickly. A man with a heart attack saved from a potentially-fatal heart rhythm by the prompt use of a defibrillator; a teenager unable to breathe because of acute severe asthma diagnosed quickly and responding to drug treatment; the first time a patient or relative shakes you by the hand and says *'thank you, doctor'*.

It is at this point that, after your years of effort and sacrifice, you realise what is the most important motivating factor: to have the knowledge, skills and attitudes that encourage someone else to seek your opinion and put their trust and their health in you. It is indeed a privilege to be a doctor.

For the student who enters medicine anticipating a lifetime of commitment and service to patients, a medical career will be most exciting, satisfying and challenging. Anyone who chooses medicine for some other reason will quickly become disillusioned and uninterested. Need we add that at this point you should be examining critically what your motives for becoming a doctor really are. What made you consider medical school in the first place – status, teacher and parent pressure, TV? If you are not sure, start thinking now, because your motivation will be questioned at interview.

'It's hard work and the training and examinations continue after you quality, but there are few careers that offer the scope and variety that medicine does. If you want a stimulating working life, medicine may be for you.'

'It always surprises me how many medical students go into medicine with little idea as to why they are doing it or what it entails. It is really important to have a concept of why you want to be a doctor and the problems that that involves, because so many of the people who drop out or are unhappy are those who didn't really want to do it in the first place.'

'Don't be put off by other people telling you they wouldn't do it again. I wouldn't do it again, but I'd still do it first time round! Believe in what you want to do, but know **why** you want to do it. It's brilliant – no other course offers you so much variety.'

'Be aware that medicine is a major commitment.'

'Make sure you want to do it for **you**, not because your parents or your school think you ought to.'

'Really **want** to study medicine – don't do it just to keep other people happy.'

'Medicine is not like ER or Peak Practice – there is a lot of routine work.'

'Carefully consider your reasons for wanting to do medicine. Don't be pushed into a choice you may not necessarily wish to do, as the course is testing and if you're not fully committed you may resent it.'

Choosing your sixth-form options

The 'traditional' requirement for medical school entry in England and Wales is three A level subjects with good grades. Preferred combinations of subjects have been:

- Chemistry with Physics and Biology (or Zoology);
- Chemistry with Physics and Mathematics;
- Chemistry with Physics and one other A level (this may be an 'Arts' subject);
- Chemistry with another Science and an Arts A level;
- Chemistry, another Science A level and two AS levels;
- Physical Science and two other A levels (but not Chemistry or Biology).

The Scottish medical schools accept A levels or five good Scottish Highers. Some medical schools may be prepared to accept other qualifications, so you should check the prospectus carefully if you are thinking of offering anything other than the traditional subjects.

Whichever subject combination you decide to take, to stand a good chance of winning a university place it is essential that you get good grades. Most achieve this by opting for subjects which they are good at and enjoy doing. If these coincide with the general requirements of medical school, your sixth-form options are easy. If not, you must decide which subjects will give you the best grades. Questions that potential students often ask include:

Which A levels will best improve my chances?

Entrance panels will accept almost any A level as evidence of academic ability. If you do plan to offer an unusual subject, it is better to contact the Admissions Officer to make sure that this is acceptable.

MUST I DO CHEMISTRY?

Chemistry is an almost universal requirement. If you do not offer Chemistry at A level, you may offer either Chemistry at AS level or Physical Science.

SHOULD I DO MATHEMATICS OR BIOLOGY?

It really doesn't matter which you choose. Mathematicians need not worry that they will miss out on essential information they will require during their medical studies – most students agree that you will soon catch up with any Biologists on your course.

MUST I OFFER A LEVELS?

The majority of students will come from UK schools where A levels (or Scottish Highers) are the commonest course followed in the sixth form. Because increasing numbers of overseas students are applying to train in the United Kingdom, the range of acceptable qualifications is increasing. Some schools already accept the European Baccalaureate, the International Baccalaureate or the BTEC Higher Diploma. Advanced GNVQ subjects are relatively new, so some universities have no fixed policy on these yet.

'I would advise anyone to take A level Biology even if it is not mandatory for the course, because students are at a disadvantage if they have not done it.'

'I didn't do A level Biology and have had no problems at all.'

'Mathematics and Physics are very appropriate for the basic medical sciences. Mathematics, if done, should incorporate statistics.'

If you intend offering any qualification or subject which is 'non-standard', always contact the Admissions Officers at the medical schools you may wish to apply to. They will be happy to advise you about the suitability (or otherwise) of your subject choice, ensuring that you will not lose out on the opportunity to apply when the time comes to fill out your UCAS form.

Mature students

The average age at entry to medical school is 18 or 19, but most medical schools have a few students aged over 21. These 'mature' students generally:

- make up less than 10% of all medical school entrants;
- have decided on a medical career much later than most students;
- are usually financially independent of their parents;
- often hold a first degree or an equivalent professional qualification;
- achieve results in the top quartile of their group;
- are highly motivated.

There is no doubt that competition for medical school places is tougher for mature students than for school-leavers, but you should feel encouraged that:

- entry requirements may be a little lower than for sixth formers in appropriate circumstances;
- entry is on merit – back up a first degree taken several years earlier with evidence of recent study;
- forms of study other than A level may be considered;
- some schools take an active interest in older students – check each prospectus carefully.

While a few medical schools reserve up to 10% of places for mature students, do not assume your chances of success must be better, as the competition for these places is fierce. Most medical schools are prepared to discuss opportunities for mature students individually. Some schools provide additional information: Nottingham, for example, has a mature students' guild to offer advice, while Leicester provides detailed guidance in a special booklet.

The questions that you will be asked at interview will be quite different from those asked of the school-leaver applicant. You will need to be well prepared so that you can convince the panel that:

- your reasons for deciding to change from your present career are sound;
- you are sufficiently motivated to complete the course and follow a career in medicine;
- you can finance your course satisfactorily without interfering with your studies.

This final point brings us to the question of obtaining funding for your studies.

In previous years, mature students have been eligible for grants and the payment of tuition fees only under certain well-defined circumstances. All this is likely to change as a result of the Dearing report into higher education (see page 107). At the time of writing, the implications of the Dearing report for the funding of mature students remain uncertain, although it seems likely that maintaining an adequate income is going to be an even greater challenge than before. We suggest you obtain up-to-date clarification of the latest proposals from your LEA at the earliest opportunity.

SUPPLEMENTING YOUR INCOME

No course is cheap and you will need to bring in extra money to make ends meet. Your reasonable options are:

- taking out a student loan each year;
- borrowing from your parents and others;
- earning money during vacations – this is attractive for those with a professional qualification;
- considering an application to one of the Armed Services for a studentship;
- applying to one of the grant-awarding bodies (see Further Reading).

Difficulties during the course

Most mature students experience similar difficulties to other students during their training – the volume of work is great and assessments usually frequent. Mature students should be aware that there may be other problems:

- there is an age gap which may present difficulties;
- married students have specific family responsibilities which may detract from study;
- there is a loss of status for those in a profession or who have held positions of responsibility;
- lack of money may be more acute than for other students.

If you are 'mature' and you intend competing for a place in medical school, make sure that you can satisfy the academic and the financial aspects of your application by seeking advice early.

Finally

If you have read *Getting into Medicine* to this point, you have declared more than a passing interest in medicine as a career. We recommend that you read on and learn how to earn your place at medical school – the first step towards you too discovering the privilege of being a doctor.

CHAPTER TWO

Choosing a medical school

Having decided that you want to be a doctor, the next step is to choose a medical school. In the following chapter you will find a description of each of the 26 medical schools in the UK. But how do you choose between them – and, indeed, find one that will be keen to choose *you*?

Every medical school has its own unique features. Not only are they based in different locations, but their courses differ in length, content and character. Some of the variation between courses is now disappearing as a result of the GMC report *Tomorrow's Doctors*, described below and in appendix 1. Nonetheless, there are still significant differences to be found and you need to consider these when deciding where to study, together with some other key factors:

- entry requirements;
- course emphasis;
- location;
- intercalated degrees;
- elective period;
- length of course;
- interview policy.

> 'It's probably true that you'll enjoy yourself wherever you go, but since you're going to be there for at least five years it is worth thinking about quite carefully.'
>
> 'At the end of the day you are trained to be a doctor wherever you go, so don't feel bad for choosing a medical school just because of where it is, or because of a small, different, part of the course that appeals.'
>
> 'Get hold of the prospectus and, if available, the faculty handbook. Don't make the mistake of assuming that all medical schools and courses are the same.'

Myths & misconceptions

There are many myths and misconceptions about getting into medical school, many of which are no longer true (even if they ever were). We do not know of any medical school that nowadays automatically offers an interview to the child of one of its own graduates. Prowess at any particular sport is not a key to entry in itself, although outstanding achievement in any activity can certainly count in your favour. Unfortunately, there is some evidence of racial bias in medical school selection. One study found that applicants with non-European surnames were less likely to be interviewed than others with the same qualifications. Ethnic grouping of applicants is now being monitored by UCAS.

The medical course

What is the best way to teach medicine and to produce good doctors? What sort of course is needed to produce doctors who will practise medicine well into the next millennium? These are difficult questions to answer. Despite generations of medical students and numerous models of training, the perfect medical course has, in the opinion of many, proved elusive. But what *is* a perfect medical course?

At one time, choosing a medical school relied more on geographic preference than details of the course on offer. The course content and structure was fairly uniform wherever you were trained. Medical teaching was (and in some places still is) didactic and, well, *traditional*.

The traditional way

Traditionally, students spent two years studying a range of subjects, lumped together as 'basic medical sciences' or 'preclinical studies'. These subjects are considered essential to the practice of medicine and were organised by the various departments of the Faculty of Medicine, such as Anatomy, Biochemistry or Physiology, each working more or less in isolation from the rest. The student could learn about the structure of the heart, the function of the cerebral cortex and the finer points of sugar metabolism all in the same day. A stiff set of examinations signalled the end of two years of disjointed tuition. Success signalled progress to the next stage of training, failure could mean ejection from the medical school.

Next, students proceeded on to the wards and followed doctors around for three years, acquiring as much information as possible. This was the clinical part of the course, where students got a taste of 'real medicine'. At the end of the course, there was a make-or-break set of final examinations, lasting about a fortnight. Success meant you became a doctor; failure meant more tuition, more examinations.

The new medical schools

Most medical schools date back at least a century, many even longer. In setting up their courses, the newer medical schools such as Nottingham, Leicester and Southampton were not so constrained by tradition as the well-established schools, and so they had an opportunity to design a different type of course, one where students met patients very early in their training, where there was more emphasis on public health, and where examinations were conducted at regular intervals rather than at the very end of the course.

Tomorrow's Doctors

Changes to the syllabus of doctors' training is nothing new: the last great change was to stop the newly qualified doctor putting up a brass plate outside his house and be legally qualified to do almost anything he wished without further training, whether this involved delicate surgery, delivering babies or administering the most toxic of drugs. This unsatisfactory arrangement was changed by Act of Parliament in 1944, after which every newly qualified doctor spent a year working under the supervision of a senior doctor while gaining much-needed experience. Most would agree that this makes sense.

Medical training might have changed only gradually were it not for the report *Tomorrow's Doctors: Recommendations on Undergraduate Medical Education* issued by the Education Committee of the General Medical Council (GMC) in December 1993. Copies may be available at your local library or you could contact the General Medical Council at: 44 Hallam Street, London W1N 6AE.

Not only does the GMC adjudicate over doctors charged with professional misconduct, but it also monitors the training of student doctors. The GMC has been seeking to change the medical curriculum to meet the demands of a changing society, such as an ageing population, rapidly changing technology, shifting emphasis towards GP-based care and increasing chronicity of disease. You should know about some of these changes because they may influence where you apply to read medicine.

Tomorrow's Doctors proposes that students be educated to become competent junior doctors ready to benefit from specialist postgraduate training. A long-term aim is a definite limit to the amount of factual content in the course, but for now there are three goals to the revision of the curriculum:

- a common core of essential knowledge;
- special study modules selected by the student;
- a more integrated training programme.

The core curriculum

'A core curriculum encompassing the essential knowledge and skills and the appropriate attitudes to be acquired at the time of graduation ...'
Tomorrow's Doctors, GMC, 1993

The first goal is a standardisation of medical courses, with a common content through a *core curriculum* (or syllabus, if you prefer) describing the essential knowledge, skills and attitudes needed by a doctor. The core curriculum will lead to greater uniformity between different medical schools, although the GMC has stopped short of imposing a rigid 'national curriculum' on medical education.

By introducing a core curriculum, the GMC hopes that medical school training will be a better preparation for the newly qualified (pre-registration) house officer, particularly where practical skills are concerned.

Special study modules

'... special study modules will enable students to explore critically and master comprehensively subjects that excite their curiosity.'
Tomorrow's Doctors, GMC, 1993

The second goal encourages the development of diversity of individual experience through *special study modules*; these allow the student to develop a deeper insight into selected areas of medicine according to his or her particular interests. These modules will allow greater freedom of choice for students and greater variety in the medical course than ever before.

The GMC does not enforce a set number or duration of special study modules, but suggests that they should comprise around one-third of the undergraduate programme. One particular aim of the special study modules is for students to develop a questioning approach to medicine and research.

Integrated learning

'The core curriculum should be system-based, its component parts being the combined responsibility of basic scientists and clinicians integrating their contributions to a common purpose ...'
Tomorrow's Doctors, GMC, 1993

The third goal recommends that the traditional approach to medical teaching, with a preclinical course divorced from the clinical course and heavily criticised by a Committee of Inquiry in 1975, be abandoned in favour of improved integration of basic science teaching and its clinical relevance. There is no doubt that the newer medical schools had a head start, but most of the other schools are making great efforts to integrate the basic science and clinical aspects of the course, with students being exposed to patients from the outset of their course.

Integration also spans the individual disciplines themselves, with an emphasis on *system*-based teaching. This means that teaching should be based upon individual body systems (cardiovascular, respiratory and so on) rather than the more traditional approach of dividing subjects along the lines of individual disciplines, such as Anatomy and Physiology.

The number of formal lectures is being reduced, students meet patients earlier and more frequently than in the past, and the clinical relevance of factual knowledge is being highlighted more often. Students have more control over (and responsibility for) their education with the advent of student-centred learning, a method that requires considerable self-discipline.

We don't necessarily recommend you read the GMC report, although you may wish to do so. Its principal recommendations, reproduced with the permission of the GMC, can be found in appendix 1 of this book. The report contains a list of recommended *knowledge objectives* and *skills objectives*, but of greater interest to you is the emphasis placed on the development of appropriate *attitudinal objectives*, which is a new suggestion and regarded as equal in importance to the acquisition of knowledge and skills. This signals a welcome move towards involving patients in the decision-making process, reflecting partly the public's greater understanding of the nature of disease and disability and the consequences of their treatment. Some of these attitudinal objectives are:

- respect for patients and colleagues;
- recognition of patients' rights;
- approaches to learning based on curiosity;
- ability to cope with uncertainty;
- awareness of the moral and ethical responsibilities involved in individual patient care;
- awareness of need to ensure the highest possible quality of patient care;
- development of capacity for self-audit;
- awareness of personal limitations;
- willingness to use capabilities to contribute to the community through preventive medicine and health promotion;
- ability to adapt to change;
- awareness of need for continuing professional development and medical education;
- acceptance of responsibility to contribute to advancement of medical knowledge.

Whether the changes made in response to *Tomorrow's Doctors* will produce better, or even *different*, doctors remains to be seen, but courses should at the very least become more interesting.

The effect of *Tomorrow's Doctors* on medical courses

Medical schools have not traditionally been at the forefront of innovation, though the 'new' schools did introduce radically different courses in the 1970s. Unsurprisingly, *Tomorrow's Doctors* stirred up many medical school curriculum committees to review their entire courses. Most schools made fairly drastic changes and are now well advanced in restructuring the entire medical course to incorporate the GMC recommendations.

You can see for yourself how many medical schools have altered their courses by examining the prospectuses for a section which refers to 'the new medical curriculum' (such as Glasgow, Bristol, Liverpool) or to the GMC's *Tomorrow's Doctors* (such as Southampton and Leicester). Sometimes a key phrase appears: for example, you might see *'the undergraduate course was radically altered'* (Aberdeen); *'a thorough review of its medical degree scheme during the last few years'* (Cardiff); *'our course is undergoing significant transformation to bring it in line with recommendations ... by the GMC'* (Birmingham); *'our integrated medical curriculum sweeps away the traditional separation between pre-clinical and clinical teaching'* (Newcastle); *'we are at present engaged in a radical revision of our medical course ...'* (Dundee).

NO DRASTIC CHANGE – AND PROUD OF IT!

Some schools have opted not to introduce major changes to their medical courses and to retain their traditional approach to medical training. Cambridge, Oxford, Edinburgh and Manchester maintain relatively traditional training programmes. Cambridge offers a preclinical course of two years, followed by a range of courses in the third year (which can be medically-oriented or totally unrelated to medicine), and finally a three-year clinical course which may be in Cambridge, London or in the provinces. Mathematicians will realise that this course is six years long instead of five, so build up your stamina before you apply.

Although Oxford *'intend to apply* [the GMC's *Tomorrow's Doctors*] *general educational objectives to our particular way of learning and teaching, the University intends to maintain "a clear-cut division between the pre-clinical and clinical courses".'*

The other 'traditional' centres, Manchester and Edinburgh, are making some efforts to make training more clinically relevant, so you might anticipate that the course you read about in the prospectus may not be as published for long.

At Manchester, the amount of didactic teaching is being reduced and more clinically-orientated lecture demonstrations and problem-solving exercises are being introduced. Students do *'not routinely attend the teaching hospitals during these [first] two years: most of your time will be spent in and around the medical school'* but the school emphasises that *'from the onset your studies will be centred on patients and their problems'*.

At Edinburgh, students undertake a Clinical Correlation course which relates the preclinical sciences to patients. You should be aware that the traditional end-of-course examinations remain, though some departments do use continuous assessment.

THE NEW MEDICINE – WHAT EVERY POTENTIAL STUDENT SHOULD KNOW

Curriculum changes, however welcome, present *you* with a problem. How do you decide where you want to study? The new medical courses may well reduce the differences between medical schools that existed previously and lead to an increased degree of standardisation – this is because the core curriculum is more prescriptive than before. The special study modules are intended to add variety to training to suit the individual. The 'new' medical schools may have been at the forefront of radical change in medical teaching away from the traditional and towards an integrated course, but most of the older schools are changing. Newcastle, for example, has had an integrated course for several years but has made further changes following *Tomorrow's Doctors*.

It is difficult to determine at the moment how medical faculties will design courses which will have features unique to that university – schools will try to develop some aspects of the syllabus to differentiate it from the pack in order to attract candidates of ever-increasing calibre. Courses are still in the process of evolving, so by the time you get to university the course published in the prospectus may have changed quite a lot! Whatever changes take place, two important facts remain. The first is that the unnatural division between the basic medical sciences and the clinical course, and between the different disciplines, is being replaced by a more integrated course. The second is that learning medicine should be more fun than attending interminable lectures. Schools are reducing the number of lectures and increasing the opportunity for students to develop personally and professionally by promoting a spirit of enquiry, critical evaluation and desire for intellectual exploration.

When you are selecting a medical course, you will need to look further than the published prospectus. It is always a good idea to talk to any of your friends already at university, about the campus, the course if they are reading medicine, what sort of teaching methods are used, the opportunities for studying abroad (especially if you have a foreign language), the various student societies, even about the city and nightlife. Some of these are discussed below. You should also ask about special study modules – chosen by the student, these allow you to pursue aspects of the course which appeal to you the most.

No science A levels?

Almost all sixth-formers who apply to medical school anticipate high grades in at least two, and often three, science subjects. Students who have taken Arts A levels are not excluded from medical training, but they will require a thorough grounding in science before starting medical training in earnest.

Be warned, however, that there are not many places available even at those universities that offer this 'premedical' course. For instance, Bristol takes about 140 directly on to the five-year medical course, but only ten on to the premedical course; Manchester takes in about 230 with science A levels and 10–20 with Arts A levels.

You will take courses in physics, chemistry and biology but, because these tend to be planned, taught and supervised by lecturers from the Faculty of Medicine, the emphasis is on relevance to medicine and scientific

Remember: The extra year means at least **six** years of training. Don't forget to budget for this when planning your finances.

principles. Courses at Edinburgh are flexible and take into account the A levels you have: this means that you can follow selected courses from their Biological Sciences course.

Entry requirements

Before applying to a medical school, check carefully whether you meet its entry requirements. Age is a factor here – most medical schools stipulate a minimum age at entry (commonly 17 or 18 years) and you must check that you meet the regulations of the medical schools that interest you.

Mature and graduate applicants should also ensure that their age will not be a barrier. Most medical schools discourage applications from those over the age of 30 years – don't waste choices on your UCAS form by applying to medical schools that will reject you outright. For example, Southampton and Leeds encourage applications from mature students and reserve 25 and 15 places a year for them, respectively, although offers are not usually made to those over 30 years of age.

Academic requirements vary between medical schools. The basic qualifications required by each medical school are listed in chapter 3, although some may be willing to provide a certain amount of flexibility. Check that your qualifications are satisfactory by consulting up-to-date copies of the prospectuses or, if necessary, by contacting the medical schools directly. This is particularly important if your qualifications are 'non-standard' – for example Scottish Highers or the Baccalaureate – as these are accepted by some institutions but not others.

Medical schools also vary in the typical A level (or SCE Highers) offers that they make to applicants. There is little point in applying for a medical school that routinely makes offers of AAA if you only expect to achieve BBB in your A level examinations. Be realistic about your abilities and draw up your shortlist of choices accordingly. Similarly, resit candidates should check what grades will be required of them at a second attempt (these are invariably higher than those offered for a first attempt). In addition, many medical schools are unwilling to consider resit candidates unless their initial poor performance was the result of extenuating circumstances.

As we said in chapter 1, you should choose your A level subjects with care so that you don't inadvertently restrict (or even rule out) your opportunities to study medicine. However, what happens if you have only decided to become a doctor *after* starting your A levels?

Eight medical schools offer one-year **premedical courses** for candidates who have performed well in 'Arts' A levels but lack the necessary science

'Check the minimum academic requirements to get into a university of your choice: then you can start getting fired up for the exams early.'

'The grades required for entrance are not necessarily an indication of how good the medical school is.'

subjects for direct entry to the medical course:

Bristol	Manchester
Dundee	Newcastle
Edinburgh	Sheffield
London – King's College	Wales

In addition, Queen's University Belfast offers a premedical year, but this is aimed at candidates with broadly-based qualifications (such as the Irish Leaving Certificate or Scottish Highers) and candidates with A levels would not be eligible. Candidates for the premedical year at Belfast should apply via the standard (A100) course code.

Relatively few places are available on premedical courses and so competition is fierce. An alternative is to consider changing A level subjects – if it's not too late to do so – or going on to study the required subjects at college after leaving school.

Medical requirements

As a medical student, you will be expected to be mentally rather than physically agile – your time is pretty much your own to use as you wish, to gain experience in your own way. Once you qualify as a doctor, you will need to be reasonably fit because your pace of life will quicken noticeably. In particular, you will:

- work long hours at a time (although things are improving here);
- be on your feet most of the time;
- frequently miss coffee breaks and meals;
- probably attend patients on wards scattered throughout the hospital;
- be a member of the cardiac arrest team which responds to medical emergencies wherever they occur in the hospital.

This does not mean that you should not consider applying for medicine if you suffer from some form of physical disability. The nature of your disability will determine whether it is feasible to contemplate a career in medicine. Universities will consider you on academic grounds, but you should contact the Admissions Office early in order to discuss your needs and options.

It is now recommended that medical students are immunised against Hepatitis B at the start of their training and that their response to the immunisation is checked. The requirements of each medical school vary in this regard. Some medical schools require evidence of immunisation against Hepatitis B (or non-infectivity) before registration as a medical student; others test all students after admission (but may refuse entry to all or part of the course to students found to be infectious carriers). Some medical schools also check immunity to tuberculosis and rubella. Ascertain the regulations of the medical schools you wish to apply to and contact your general practitioner as early as possible to check your immune status and arrange immunisation as appropriate.

Course emphasis

As we said earlier, the differences between medical curricula have become less distinct since the advent of the GMC report *Tomorrow's Doctors*. There is now a greater emphasis on systems-based teaching, in which the basic sciences are taught in an integrated way according to body systems (e.g. respiratory system, circulatory system, etc.) rather than along the traditional divisions of anatomy, biochemistry and so forth.

The greater integration also extends to the increasingly blurred division between preclinical and clinical teaching, with most universities now introducing students to patients from the beginning of their course. Nonetheless, some medical schools, most notably Oxford and Cambridge, still retain a strong emphasis on the basic sciences. Further details of their courses can be found in chapter 3. St Andrews also emphasises the basic sciences, partly by virtue of the fact that it has no clinical school (students transfer to Manchester to complete their training).

In addition to looking at how you will be *taught*, it is important to consider how you will be *assessed*. A wide variety of assessment methods have been introduced to medical school curricula over the last few years, many of which are described in more detail in chapter 10. Look at the emphasis of each medical school's assessment methods (e.g. continuous

'Look for the style of course that will suit you, good accommodation and a friendly atmosphere.'

'There are considerable differences between medical courses. In particular, note if dissection is carried out, if there is continuous assessment or one big examination, and the amount of independent work (a feature of new courses).'

'The biggest difference between medical schools is whether the course is traditional or integrated. I prefer the traditional system, as the preclinical years give you time to sort out your basic sciences and to mature to be able to cope with clinical training. I would have hated to start medical school straight away dealing with patients. On the other hand, many of my peers were frustrated with having to go through two years without meeting a single patient. So it depends on what you want.'

'Find out about how the course is assessed. Do you do better in examinations or in-course assessment?'

assessment versus end-of-year examinations) and think about which method you prefer.

Despite the overall similarity of the medical curriculum at most universities, significant differences can be found on closer inspection. A number of medical schools now offer opportunities for study in mainland Europe. At Manchester, for example, there is a European Programme which allows around ten students each year with a working knowledge of French and/or German to undertake part of their studies in France, Germany or Switzerland. The University even provides 'out of hours' language tutorials during the first three years to help maintain language skills.

Location

The location of your medical school is important in many respects and may have life-long consequences, as many doctors settle down and practise close to their medical school. It is therefore sensible to invest some thought and effort into your decision-making process.

Do you want to live near your home town or as far away as possible? There are good arguments for moving away from your parents and other relatives, not least because going to university represents an important step on the road to your independence. However, students with family or other commitments may need to stay close to home – this is often a factor for mature students.

The social life you enjoy at university will depend upon many factors, but living in central London will clearly present you with different opportunities to living in Dundee. Consider whether you want to live in a major city like London, Birmingham or Manchester, or a smaller university-oriented city like Oxford, Cambridge or St Andrews. Would you like to

'Consider the type of course, the nature of the institution and the geographical position. Geography may seem less important when you are keen to leave home, but after a few years, when the holidays are shorter and the pressure rises, proximity to home matters a bit more.'

'Go by the feel of the place. In general, if you like the look and feel of the place you will be able to fit in.'

'Decide if you can afford to study in London (if you cannot it will cut your options). I think the most important thing is to pick a city you want to live in for five or more years.'

'The course is important but find out about other activities that you may also want to do, such as sport or music.'

'Remember, it is not what the medical school does for you, but what you manage to get out of the medical school. You make things happen for yourself.'

be near the coast or the countryside? How easy will it be to travel home or to see friends elsewhere? All these considerations form a part of the equation.

Consider the living costs of each location, too. It is more expensive to live in London than in Oxford, and more expensive in Oxford than in Manchester. The university's accommodation office will give you information about the cost of renting a room in its student housing, and a visit to the city will give you an opportunity to weigh up rental prices in the private sector as well as overall living costs.

Intercalated degrees

All medical schools, with the exception of Sheffield, offer students the opportunity to study for an additional degree, usually a BSc or BMedSci, by taking an extra (*intercalated*) year's study. Intercalated degrees are not open to all, but only to those deemed suitable according to their academic performance. The number of students taking an optional intercalated degree varies considerably between medical schools, from around 10% up to 60%.

Oxford, Cambridge and Nottingham already include an additional degree as a compulsory component of the course, and this is also planned at Imperial College School of Medicine. At St Andrews, the three-year course leads to a general BSc (Medical Science) degree, but selected students can take an intercalated fourth year to study for an Honours BSc (Medical Science).

> ### Intercalated degree
>
> An intercalated degree is an additional degree (commonly a BSc) taken during the medical course. Students who take an intercalated degree will therefore have an additional qualification. The degree usually requires one year of research-based work, culminating in the submission of a dissertation. After completing the degree, the student returns to the medical course. More information on intercalated degrees can be found in chapter 8.

Elective period

Most universities offer a single elective period of around eight to twelve weeks, during which students are encouraged to travel elsewhere to gain experience of medical practice in a different setting, usually abroad.

At Aberdeen, students undertake two eight-week elective periods. One of these is devoted to a project on a medical topic and is usually taken abroad. The other allows students to study a non-medical topic, such as a language or business skills, that may be useful in their professional life.

As a preclinical medical school, St Andrews has no elective period of its own. However, students transfer to Manchester for the clinical course and undertake an eight-week elective period from there.

> ### Elective period
>
> The elective period is traditionally one of the most popular parts of the medical course. Usually eight to twelve weeks in duration, it is an opportunity for the student to pursue a medical subject of interest, usually in a foreign country. A wide variety of electives are now available at different medical schools. More information on elective periods can be found in chapter 9.

Length of course

There is little variation in the length of the course between different medical schools, the majority being five years in duration. The medical course lasts six years at Oxford, and also at St Andrews (where the three-year preclinical course is followed by three years on the clinical course at Manchester). At Cambridge the overall length of the course depends upon where the clinical course is undertaken – it is five and a quarter years in Cambridge, and six years if students transfer elsewhere. At other universities, study for an intercalated degree will usually add one year to the length of the course, although the Nottingham medical course lasts just five years despite the inclusion of a period of study for a BMedSci degree.

Interview policy

Most medical schools routinely interview applicants before making them an offer, but six do not (see chapter 5). If you are concerned about your abilities at interview, you could make your choices from these alone. However, it is often a pity to restrict your selection in this way, and you should give careful thought as to whether, in the long term, this is the best strategy. Indeed, anyone who doubts their abilities at interview should think carefully about their choice of medicine as a career, as it requires excellent communication skills. This issue is discussed in more detail in chapter 5.

You should also bear in mind the fact that 'non-standard' applicants (mature or graduate students, for example) are rarely made offers without an interview, regardless of the medical school's general policy.

What next?

Having decided which factors are going to influence your choice of medical school, go on to find out as much as you can about what they each have to offer. Ensure that your choice is a well-informed one. This book will start you off on this process, but study other guides too and the medical school prospectuses themselves. Read the information contained in the prospectuses with a critical eye, though. University prospectuses are, after all, really just a form of advertising and are written to promote the universities' best features.

Personal recommendations from parents, teachers, doctors and careers advisers can also prove helpful but must also be assessed objectively – much of their information is likely to be outdated. Some of the best advice comes from current students, and you should make an effort to get in touch with as many as possible. Find out who has left your school to study medicine in the last few years, or arrange visits (where possible) to the medical schools that interest you.

'Visit the medical schools you are interested in, browse the prospectus, ask around and talk to friends who are at university.'

'It's a good idea to visit as many medical schools as possible.'

CHAPTER THREE

A guide to the UK medical schools

On the following pages you will find a detailed entry for each of the 26 medical schools in the UK. Although we hope that this information will help you to compile your application shortlist, we strongly recommend that you also consult an up-to-date prospectus before making any final decisions. You will find advice on applying for prospectuses in appendix 2, together with a list of addresses for each university or medical school.

We have tried to standardise the information provided in this chapter so that you can compare medical school courses more easily. Each listing begins with a contact address which should *not*, in general, be used for straightforward prospectus requests, but is likely to be useful if you have a specific query about the course or the suitability of your qualifications. You will also find telephone (☎) and Fax numbers where available.

The UCAS code is given for most medical schools, although you should note that this is liable to change, especially as the London medical schools merge. Always check the appropriate course codes in a current copy of the *UCAS Handbook* before you complete your UCAS form.

All the institutions listed have home pages on the World Wide Web, where you will often find further information, together with students' homepages that can give you a useful 'insider's view' of the university or medical school. A World Wide Web address is therefore included with each entry.

The main part of each entry contains background information about the medical school followed by a summary of key features of the curriculum. We have also described the main methods of assessment used during the course, together with details of intercalated degree courses and the elective period.

In the **Entry Requirements** section, we have listed the most important entry requirements for each medical school. However, many have additional requirements and sometimes several subject permutations are possible. There may also be a certain amount of flexibility with the minimum requirements, depending upon your individual circumstances. We are unable to include every detail in our listings and you should check the relevant prospectus for the most up-to-date entry requirements. This is particularly relevant for applicants offering non-standard qualifications (such as International or European Baccalaureate, Irish Leaving Certificate, BTEC National and Higher National Diplomas, Advanced GNVQ and so on). For medical schools in Scotland we have included their SCE Higher examination requirements. For information about the acceptability of SCE Highers at medical schools outside Scotland, consult the relevant prospectus or contact the medical school directly.

In the **Further Information** section we have highlighted any additional details of particular interest, such as policies towards deferred entry, mature or graduate students, or information about visit days. The **Living in ...** and **Students' Comments** sections both provide an informal insight into life at the medical school.

Finally, we have included an **At a Glance** box which summarises facts and figures relating to the course. This includes the number of applications received by the medical school, the number of offers made, the total number of students accepted and the number of overseas students accepted. These figures have been compiled with the help of the Department of Research and Statistics at UCAS and relate to applications for medicine made through UCAS in 1994–5, the latest year for which complete figures were available at the time of writing.

We have provided some general guidance on interviewing policies – the statement *'Yes'* means that candidates are usually or always interviewed before an offer is made. You should also note that the remark *'No'* generally applies only to 'straightforward' first-time school leavers. Mature applicants, overseas applicants and those with 'non-standard' qualifications are all more likely to be invited for an interview.

Information about typical A level offers is included, although you should be aware that the average grades achieved by applicants are usually higher than the typical offer. You should also note that, where medical schools are willing to consider resit candidates, a higher offer is usually made. In addition, many medical schools only consider resit candidates when significant extenuating circumstances applied to their initial failure to achieve the necessary grades.

We have also indicated medical schools that offer a premedical course for applicants who lack the necessary science A levels, and listed the overall length of the medical course, the degrees offered, and the length of the elective period.

> **Facts & figures**
>
> In 1994–5:
> - 59,445 applications in aggregate were received;
> - 12,323 offers (unconditional or conditional) were made;
> - 4639 applicants were accepted;
> - 393 accepted applicants were from outside the UK.
>
> *Source:* UCAS statistics office

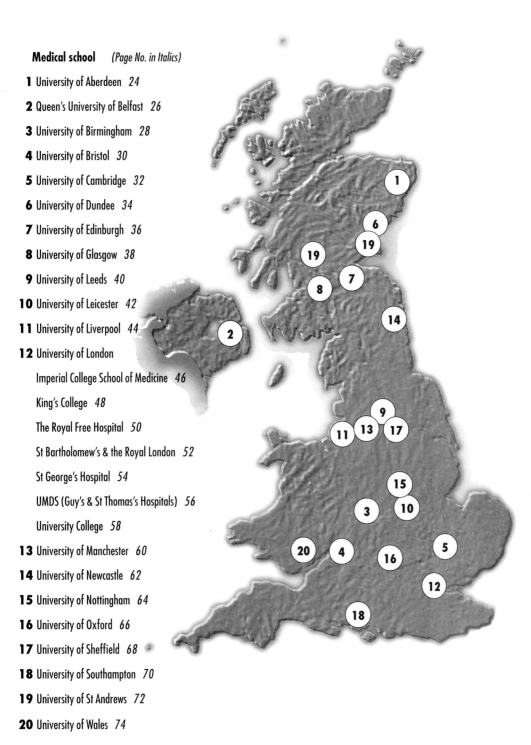

Medical school   *(Page No. in Italics)*

1 University of Aberdeen   *24*

2 Queen's University of Belfast   *26*

3 University of Birmingham   *28*

4 University of Bristol   *30*

5 University of Cambridge   *32*

6 University of Dundee   *34*

7 University of Edinburgh   *36*

8 University of Glasgow   *38*

9 University of Leeds   *40*

10 University of Leicester   *42*

11 University of Liverpool   *44*

12 University of London

    Imperial College School of Medicine   *46*

    King's College   *48*

    The Royal Free Hospital   *50*

    St Bartholomew's & the Royal London   *52*

    St George's Hospital   *54*

    UMDS (Guy's & St Thomas's Hospitals)   *56*

    University College   *58*

13 University of Manchester   *60*

14 University of Newcastle   *62*

15 University of Nottingham   *64*

16 University of Oxford   *66*

17 University of Sheffield   *68*

18 University of Southampton   *70*

19 University of St Andrews   *72*

20 University of Wales   *74*

UNIVERSITY OF ABERDEEN MEDICAL SCHOOL

UNIVERSITY OF ABERDEEN MEDICAL SCHOOL

Deputy Director of Studies (Admissions) Medicine
University of Aberdeen
Academic & General Administration Section Registry
University Office
Regent Walk
Aberdeen AB9 1FX

UCAS code: ABRDN A20 A100 MB/ChB

☎   (01224) 272035 – Deputy Director of Studies
        (01224) 272090 – School Liaison Officer
Fax: (01224) 272031 – Admissions Office
E-mail: schlia@admin.abdn.ac.uk – Schools Liaison Service
        admoff@admin.abdn.ac.uk – Admissions Office
WWW: http://www.abdn.ac.uk

A Faculty of Medicine was established in Aberdeen at the end of the fifteenth century. Currently about two-thirds of its students come from Scotland.

COURSE OUTLINE

A new curriculum commenced in 1995 and is divided into four phases, with special study modules available in each phase.

Phase I occupies Year 1 and teaches the basic medical sciences in an integrated fashion, emphasising clinical relevance. There is also a parallel community-based course in local general practices. **Phase II** covers the principles of disease, combining another systems-based course with multisystem subjects such as child health. Regular ward attendance follows clinical method teaching. Phase II lasts until two-thirds of the way through Year 3.

Phase III lasts until the end of Year 4 and consists mainly of nine five-week specialist rotations, including both systems-based and multisystem specialty attachments. **Phase IV** in the final year consists of five eight-week blocks. In three blocks students choose their clinical attachments and projects. Two remaining blocks are devoted to 'elective' study.

ASSESSMENT

'Barrier' assessments are held at the end of each phase. Interim assessments can lead to full- or part-exemption from these. No written examinations take place in Phase IV. The final decision on graduation is provided by project work in the medical elective and a patient-centred clinical assessment.

INTERCALATED DEGREE

Students of particular ability can spend one additional year on medically-related research leading to the BSc (MedSci) Honours degree. Students with appropriate language skills can spend some or all of the year in a European university.

ELECTIVE PERIOD

Two eight-week blocks are available for 'elective' study in Phase IV, one devoted to a project on a medical topic (usually taken abroad). The other allows students to study a non-medical topic.

AT A GLANCE

Applications received	**1463**
Offers made	**519**
Total accepted	**160**
Overseas accepted	**16**
Interview	**No**
Typical A level offer	**ABB**
Typical SCE Highers offer	**AAAAB**
Premedical course	**No**
Length of course	**5 years**
Degrees	**MB ChB**
Intercalated degree	**BSc (Med Sci) (optional)**
Elective period	**2 × 8 weeks**

ENTRY REQUIREMENTS

- 3 A levels **must** include Chemistry; recommended other subjects are two of Biology, Mathematics or Physics

- 5 SCE Highers must include Higher B in Chemistry and normally two of Biology, Mathematics or Physics

- must have an English Language O/Standard Grade/GCSE level pass

- SCE Highers resit candidates may be considered; A level resit candidates are not normally considered

FURTHER INFORMATION

Applicants wishing to defer entry will be considered. The Admissions Committee prefers that candidates broaden their experience, perhaps in work of a caring nature.

A 1991 video (*The Beginning of Wisdom*) is available for loan from: Schools Liaison Service, University of Aberdeen, Regent Walk, Aberdeen AB24 3FX, ☎ (01224) 272090/ 272091.

Candidates are encouraged to visit the medical school and can arrange this through the Schools Liaison Officer, ☎ (01224) 272090.

LIVING IN ABERDEEN

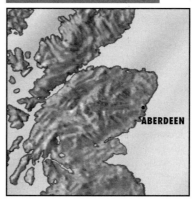

Aberdeen is located in the north-east of Scotland and has over 250,000 inhabitants, including around 10,000 students at the University. The city is well known for its granite buildings and is often referred to as the 'Granite City'. The city's prosperity is, in part, due to its role in managing the energy resources of the North Sea.

The city has a great deal to offer in terms of leisure pursuits. The proximity of the Cairngorms and Grampians is an attraction for mountaineers and skiers, and many other outdoor activities are available along the coast and the surrounding rivers. The city has an active nightlife and there are several concert halls, an Edwardian theatre and numerous restaurants and bars. There is an international airport (Aberdeen is just over one hour from London by air) and good coach and rail connections.

UNIVERSITY OF ABERDEEN MEDICAL SCHOOL

THE QUEEN'S UNIVERSITY OF BELFAST MEDICAL SCHOOL

THE QUEEN'S UNIVERSITY OF BELFAST MEDICAL SCHOOL

Admissions Officer
The Queen's University of Belfast
University Road
Belfast BT7 1NN

UCAS code: QBELF Q75 A100 MB

☎ (01232) 245133 Ext. 3099 – Dean
(01232) 245133 Ext. 3079 – Admissions Office
Fax: (01232) 247895 – Admissions Office
WWW: http://www.qub.ac.uk

Around 90% of the annual intake of about 160 come from Northern Ireland. The Queen's University of Belfast is unique in that, as well as awarding the degrees of MB and BCh, it also awards the degree of Bachelor of Obstetrics (BAO). The degree of BAO is not registrable with the General Medical Council.

COURSE OUTLINE

A premedical year is available for up to five students and is intended for those with more broadly-based qualifications than A levels (for example the Irish Leaving Certificate or Scottish Highers). There is no separate UCAS course code for the premedical year.

Students taking the premedical course attend first-year courses in chemistry, physics and biological science. Premedical students must complete this course satisfactorily before proceeding on to the medical course.

The main medical course is five years long and, in line with *Tomorrow's Doctors*, takes an integrated, problem-based, approach to medical teaching, with an emphasis on clinical skills. Students who successfully complete the medical course are awarded the degrees of MB BCh BAO. These may be awarded 'with honours', or 'with distinction' in specific subjects.

INTERCALATED DEGREE

Students may apply to take a one-year intercalated degree following the successful completion of at least two years of the course. Courses are available in anatomy, biochemistry, clinical pharmacology, medical genetics, pathology and physiology. Most intercalated degree course students also take a course in medical computing and statistics. The intercalated degree course leads to the award of an Honours BSc or BMedSc degree.

There are a limited number of MRC and LEA studentships available and, in addition, the six most distinguished students are awarded a Foundation Scholarship by the University. After the completion of a research project, intercalated degree students present the results in a dissertation.

ELECTIVE PERIOD

An elective period of six weeks' duration is usually spent abroad in the summer vacation of the final year.

AT A GLANCE

Applications received	**885**
Offers made	**352**
Total accepted	**162**
Overseas accepted	**14**
Interview	**No**
Typical A level offer	**AAB**
Premedical course	**Yes**
Length of course	**5 years***
Degrees	**MB BCh BAO**
Intercalated degree	**BSc or BMedSc (optional)**
Elective period	**6 weeks**

*(*6 years if premedical course taken)*

ENTRY REQUIREMENTS

- 3 A levels

- **must** include A level Chemistry and normally two of Biology, Mathematics and Physics

- A level Chemistry, one science subject and one other subject is also acceptable

- GCSE Mathematics, Physics and Biology (or Double Award Science) unless offered at A level

FURTHER INFORMATION

Graduate applicants should possess at least an upper second class degree. Applicants over the age of 30 years are only admitted in exceptional circumstances.

In addition to university accommodation, designated accommodation is available for medical students. Biggart House has room for 150 students although, as this is in the Royal Victoria Hospital complex, it is normally used by clinical students.

LIVING IN BELFAST

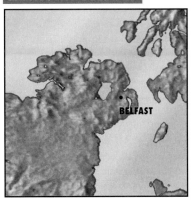

The Queen's University of Belfast has over 10,000 students working in nine separate faculties, of which medicine is one. The University is situated a mile south of the city centre and there are many nearby restaurants, shops and bars. Indeed, the entire Province of Northern Ireland is within 90 minutes' travelling time of the University.

Every November the University hosts an international arts festival with over 200 musical and theatrical performances. The University also owns a two-screen cinema known as the 'QFT' (Queen's Film Theatre), which regularly screens major international movies.

For outdoor pursuits, the Mourne mountains are nearby, as are many miles of coastline and the largest lake in Europe.

THE QUEEN'S UNIVERSITY OF BELFAST MEDICAL SCHOOL

UNIVERSITY OF BIRMINGHAM MEDICAL SCHOOL

UNIVERSITY OF BIRMINGHAM MEDICAL SCHOOL
The Admissions Tutor
Medical School
The University of Birmingham
Edgbaston
Birmingham B15 2TT

UCAS code: BIRM B32 A100 MBChB/Med

☎   (0121) 414 6888 – Medicine enquiries
           (0121) 414 3374 – Admissions
Fax: (0121) 414 3850 – Admissions
E-mail: prospectus@bham.ac.uk – Prospectus requests
WWW: http://www.bham.ac.uk

West Midlands region is the largest in the country, with a population of 5.5 million and a number of different hospitals. Birmingham Medical School is located at the Queen Elizabeth Medical Centre, two minutes from the university campus.

COURSE OUTLINE

As elsewhere, the curriculum is undergoing changes in line with the GMC report *Tomorrow's Doctors,* and so the following details are subject to change. **Year 1** begins with a foundation course and is followed by two years of teaching centred around the systems of the body. There is also teaching about the psychology and sociology of health and illness, public health and medical ethics. One day per fortnight is spent in general practice. The first of a number of special study modules is undertaken towards the end of **Year 2**, allowing study of a chosen subject in depth.

A foundation course in clinical science comes at the start of **Year 3**, followed by a clinical introductory course. Students then undertake junior clinical attachments in medicine and surgery. A series of subspecialty attachments are then taken, followed by a two-month elective period leading to the end of **Year 4**. **Year 5** is devoted to senior student attachments in medicine and surgery, and also attachments in obstetrics & gynaecology, psychiatry, paediatrics and general practice.

ASSESSMENT

Each stage of the medical course is subject to continuous assessment, including end-of-semester examinations and submitted course work. An assessment is held at the end of each attachment in Year 5, but there is not a traditional 'Finals' examination.

INTERCALATED DEGREE

Subject to an adequate performance in their examinations, students may be considered for a one-year intercalated degree course. This leads to a bachelor's degree in one of the Honours Schools of Medical Sciences.

ELECTIVE PERIOD

Students spend two months in the spring of Year 4 undertaking an elective period, which can be in the medical school, elsewhere in the UK or abroad. A number of competitive bursaries are available.

AT A GLANCE

Applications received	**1995**
Offers made	**417**
Total accepted	**194**
Overseas accepted	**12**
Interview	**Yes**
Typical A level offer	**ABB**
Premedical course	**No**
Length of course	**5 years**
Degrees	**MB ChB**
Intercalated degree	**Optional**
Elective period	**2 months**

ENTRY REQUIREMENTS

- 3 A levels which **must** include A level Chemistry, with A level Biology, Mathematics or Physics (Biology preferred), and one other subject (**not** General Studies)

- Human Biology or Zoology may be offered instead of Biology (but not in combination)

- 2 AS levels may be offered in lieu of the third A level

- GCSE English Language (grade C minimum)

- GCSE Biology, Mathematics and Physics (grade B minimum) unless offered at A level

- Integrated Science (double certification) may be substituted for Biology and Physics at grade B minimum

- minimum of 8 GCSEs at good grades

FURTHER INFORMATION

Applications are welcomed from mature candidates. However, those aged 30 years or more at the time of proposed entry are not normally considered.

About 10% of students defer entry for a year. The medical school recommends that the year is spent by *'working, travelling, voluntary service or some activity'*. It does not have to be directly related to medicine.

UNIVERSITY OF BIRMINGHAM MEDICAL SCHOOL

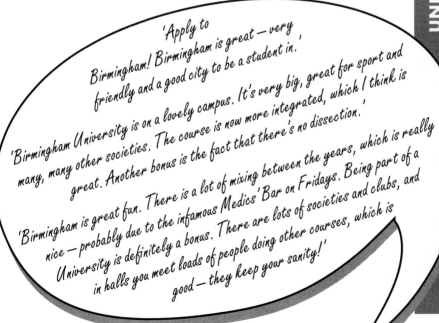

'Apply to Birmingham! Birmingham is great – very friendly and a good city to be a student in.'

'Birmingham University is on a lovely campus. It's very big, great for sport and many, many other societies. The course is now more integrated, which I think is great. Another bonus is the fact that there's no dissection.'

'Birmingham is great fun. There is a lot of mixing between the years, which is really nice – probably due to the infamous Medics' Bar on Fridays. Being part of a University is definitely a bonus. There are lots of societies and clubs, and in halls you meet loads of people doing other courses, which is good – they keep your sanity!'

UNIVERSITY OF BRISTOL MEDICAL SCHOOL

Undergraduate Admissions Office
University of Bristol
Senate House
Tyndall Avenue
Bristol BS8 1TH

UCAS code: BRISL B78 A104 MB/ChB6 (6 year course)
             BRISL B78 A106 MB/ChB5 (5 year course)

☎   (0117) 928 7679 – Medical Admissions Clerk
Fax: (0117) 925 1424
E-mail: Admissions@bris.ac.uk
WWW: http://www.bris.ac.uk

The Faculty of Medicine in Bristol includes the schools of dentistry and
veterinary science as well as the school of medicine. Clinical teaching takes
place at hospitals in Bristol and the surrounding area, away from the School
of Medical Sciences.

COURSE OUTLINE

In common with many medical schools, the GMC recommendations led to the introduction of a new medical curriculum in 1995. The curriculum lasts five years, although a one-year premedical course (A104) is available for students without the necessary science A levels. Ten students were accepted on to A104 from 345 applicants in 1994–5.

Phase 1 of the course lasts two terms and acts as an introduction to basic medical science and behavioural science. Exposure to patients is a feature of the course from the outset. **Phase 2** of the course lasts until the end of Year 3. Formal teaching of the body systems combines integrated preclinical and clinical input, and includes full-time clinical attachments. In **Phase 3** students continue clinical teaching in hospitals both in Bristol and the South West, together with experience in the community. Teaching is often by means of small-group tutorials during the course, accompanied by self-directed learning. Bedside and clinic teaching takes place during the clinical attachments. Optional special study modules are available.

ASSESSMENT

Examinations occur throughout the course and these normally take place at the end of each year. There is also a contribution from continuous assessment. There is a written examination at the end of Year 1 and a professional examination at the end of Year 3. The final MB ChB examination is held at the end of Year 5.

INTERCALATED DEGREE

It may be possible to transfer to the Faculty of Science for one year at the end of Year 2 to work towards a BSc (Hons) intercalated degree. Provision of financial assistance may be possible for some students.

ELECTIVE PERIOD

The European Credit Transfer Scheme provides an opportunity to spend three months to one year at participating medical schools in Europe and be credited for the work undertaken there.

AT A GLANCE

Applications received	**2194 (A106)**
Offers made	**380 (A106)**
Total accepted	**140 (A106)**
Overseas accepted	**13 (A106)**
Interview	**Yes**
Typical A level offer	**ABB**
Typical A+AS level offer	**AB + BB**
Premedical course	**Yes**
Length of course	**5 years***
Degrees	**MB ChB**
Intercalated degree	**BSc (optional)**

(*6 years if premedical course taken)

ENTRY REQUIREMENTS

- 3 A levels **or** 2 A + 2 AS levels

- **must** include A level Chemistry plus two of Physics, Mathematics and Biology (or Zoology)

- candidates with one approved non-science subject are given equal consideration

- 6 grade As at GCSE level usually required for pre-A level applicants

- knowledge of a European language is welcome for participation in the European Credit Transfer Scheme

FURTHER INFORMATION

Students wishing to defer entry for one year are given encouragement. The Faculty of Medicine will be interested to know how applicants intend to spend the year.

Applicants with relevant work experience are encouraged to apply, although those over the age of 30 years are not normally considered.

A Preview Day is held annually for prospective applicants. For further information contact the Medical Admissions Clerk at the Undergraduate Admissions Office.

LIVING IN BRISTOL

BRISTOL

Bristol is one of the most lively cities in the South West and is an important centre of industry and commerce. It is also one of the most attractive, with many acres of parks and gardens and being within easy reach of the surrounding countryside.

Further afield are the city of Bath and the coastal resorts of Clevedon and Weston-super-Mare. London is about two hours away by road and there is a local airport with good national and international connections.

There is a strong Arts scene and an excellent selection of pubs and restaurants. Sports are also well-represented: there are two league football teams, a rugby union team and the Gloucestershire cricket team.

UNIVERSITY OF BRISTOL MEDICAL SCHOOL

UNIVERSITY OF CAMBRIDGE MEDICAL SCHOOL

UNIVERSITY OF CAMBRIDGE MEDICAL SCHOOL
Cambridge Intercollegiate Applications Office
Kellet Lodge
Tennis Court Road
Cambridge CB2 1QJ

UCAS code: CAM C05 A100 MB/BChir

☎   (01223) 333308 – CIAO
Fax: (01223) 366383 – CIAO
E-mail: ucam-undergraduate-admissions@lists.cam.ac.uk
WWW: http://www.cam.ac.uk

The Cambridge medical course aims to train doctors *'for compassionate as well as scientific practice'* (Undergraduate Prospectus 1997–8). Applications are usually made direct to a college and may involve a written (or 'STEP') examination in addition to an interview. The university prospectus contains further details about the application procedure as well as individual college descriptions.

COURSE OUTLINE
The three preclinical years are devoted to the Medical Sciences Tripos. During this time the student is based in Cambridge.

Year 1 is spent studying anatomy, biochemistry, medical genetics and physiology for Part IA of the Tripos. During this time students also take the Second MB course in population sciences. **Year 2** is devoted to further studies in anatomy and physiology, together with neurobiology, pathology, pharmacology, psychology and reproductive biology for Part IB of the Tripos.

A wide choice of subjects is available for study in **Year 3**, leading to a BA degree. These include not only medically-related subjects but also law, art and others. Students then decide whether to stay on in Cambridge for the clinical course (which lasts a further 2¼ years) or to apply to one of the London or provincial medical schools (where the course lasts 3 years).

Students staying in Cambridge take a three-part Final MB examination, comprising pathology, obstetrics & gynaecology, and medicine & surgery. One unusual aspect of the Cambridge course is that its students graduate in December.

ASSESSMENT
Exemption from Second MB examinations is gained by achieving a satisfactory standard in the Part IA and IB Tripos examinations in Years 1 and 2. Assessment in the clinical course will depend upon where it is undertaken.

INTERCALATED DEGREE
The three-year preclinical period, spent in Cambridge reading the Medical Sciences Tripos, leads to a BA degree. The Cambridge Clinical School also offers an MB/PhD programme combining three years of research with the clinical training.

ELECTIVE PERIOD
The nature and duration of the elective period will depend upon where the clinical course is undertaken.

AT A GLANCE

Applications received	**993**
Offers made	**305**
Total accepted	**237**
Overseas accepted	**26**
Interview	**Yes**
Typical A level offer	**AAA**
Premedical course	**No**
Length of course	**5¼ years***
Degrees	**BA MB BChir**
Intercalated degree	**BA (compulsory)**
Elective period	**See previous page**

*(*6 years if clinical course taken elsewhere)*

ENTRY REQUIREMENTS

- 3 A levels **or** 2 A + 2 AS levels

- **must** include A level Chemistry

- **must** also include 1 A level, **or** 2 AS levels, from Biology, Mathematics or Physics

- GCSE passes (grade C or above) in Biology, Mathematics and Physics if not offered at A or AS level

- a pass in double award Science may be substituted for GCSE Biology and Physics

- various equivalent examinations are acceptable – see the prospectus for more information

FURTHER INFORMATION

Application to Cambridge (and Oxford) starts earlier than for other universities – consult an up-to-date copy of the prospectus for more details. Further information on the medical course is available from the College Admissions Offices. To arrange a visit, contact the relevant college or colleges in advance.

A video on University Entry (for sale or loan) can be obtained from Cambridge Intercollegiate

Applications Office (CIAO), address on previous page. An alternative prospectus can be obtained for £4.00 (UK) from: Cambridge University Students' Union, 11–12 Trumpington Street, Cambridge CB2 1QA, ☎ (01223) 333313.

LIVING IN CAMBRIDGE

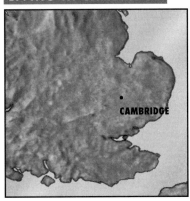

Cambridge was founded in the 1220s by scholars fleeing Oxford. The University dominates the city even now, most tangibly in the many colleges. It is a small and attractive city, particularly around the stretch of land (known as 'the Backs') that runs alongside the Cam.

Plenty of social and sporting activities are available for students in Cambridge, with over 250 societies that include the Union Debating Society and the Footlights. The city also has a number of theatres, a popular arts cinema and many pubs and restaurants. An international arts festival and a folk festival are annual events. The countryside lies just outside the city, and further afield are the towns of Grantchester, Saffron Walden and Newmarket.

UNIVERSITY OF CAMBRIDGE MEDICAL SCHOOL

UNIVERSITY OF DUNDEE MEDICAL SCHOOL

UNIVERSITY OF DUNDEE MEDICAL SCHOOL
Student Recruitment Service
University of Dundee
Nethergate
Dundee DD1 4HN

UCAS code: DUND D65 A100 MB/ChB
               DUND D65 A104 MB/ChBP (premedical year)

☎   (01382) 344697 – Course enquiries
         (01382) 344160 – General advice & visits
Fax: (01382) 221554
E-mail: srs@dundee.ac.uk
WWW: http://www.dundee.ac.uk

Medical teaching began at Dundee in 1887. A new purpose-built teaching hospital and medical school was opened in 1974 at Ninewells, which is approximately 4 kilometres from the main university precinct.

COURSE OUTLINE

A one-year premedical course (A104) is available for those who do not have the necessary science qualifications to enter the medical course directly. Seven students were accepted on to A104 from 252 applicants in 1994–5.

As with most other medical schools, Dundee has revised its course in line with *Tomorrow's Doctors*. The new integrated and systematic course is made up of three phases.

Phase 1 occupies the first year and is concerned with normal structure, function and behaviour and, although based around the basic medical sciences, it is intended that students will gain clinical experience from the outset. Self-directed learning now forms an important part of the course. For Years 2 and 3, **Phase 2** of the course moves on to consider abnormal structure, function and behaviour with a systematic study of clinical medicine. **Phase 3** (in Years 4 and 5) applies the skills and knowledge acquired in Phases 1 and 2 in a clinical setting. As with Phase 1, self-directed learning forms an integral part of this stage of the course.

ASSESSMENT

There is a strong emphasis on integrated and interdisciplinary continuous assessment which focuses on clinical relevance rather than simple rote learning. 'Stopping examinations' (based mainly around continuous assessment) occur at the end of each phase of the course.

INTERCALATED DEGREE

Depending upon their performance, students can be selected for a one-year intercalated BMSc Honours degree. This is usually undertaken between Phases 2 and 3.

ELECTIVE PERIOD

An elective period of up to 10 weeks is available in the final year of study and can be taken anywhere in the world. Assistance with travelling expenses is available on a competitive basis.

AT A GLANCE

Applications received	**1415 (A100)**
Offers made	**422 (A100)**
Total accepted	**130 (A100)**
Overseas accepted	**15 (A100)**
Interview	**No**
Typical A level offer	**ABB**
Typical SCE Highers offer	**AAABB**
Premedical course	**Yes**
Length of course	**5 years***
Degrees	**MB ChB**
Intercalated degree	**BMSc (optional)**
Elective period	**10 weeks**

(*6 years if premedical course taken)

ENTRY REQUIREMENTS

- A level grades ABB **or** SCE Highers grades AAABB

- includes Chemistry and normally two from Biology (or Human Biology), Physics and Mathematics

- Physical Science A level meets requirements for Chemistry and Physics, but counts as only one of the three A levels required

- several other complex combinations are possible – consult the prospectus for details

FURTHER INFORMATION

A one-year premedical course is available for those who do not meet the requirements for direct entry to the medical course. Usually fewer than 10 places are available.

All single students are guaranteed university accommodation in their first year. University open days and Pre-Application Visit Days are organised. For further information contact the Student Recruitment Service at the address on the previous page, ☎ (01382) 344160.

LIVING IN DUNDEE

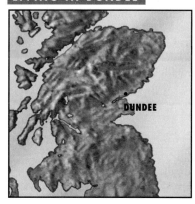

The city of Dundee, with its population of 160,000 (including a full-time student population of 6700), lies on the Tay estuary on the east coast of Scotland. Dundee has undergone many changes in its history and now has a significant role in the technology industry.

Dundee University has a lively campus located ten minutes' walk from the city centre. Many social, sporting and artistic activities are available on-site. The city itself offers a number of museums and art galleries, two major theatres and a regional film theatre. Further afield are the Grampian mountains with opportunities for walking, climbing and skiing.

UNIVERSITY OF DUNDEE MEDICAL SCHOOL

UNIVERSITY OF EDINBURGH MEDICAL SCHOOL

UNIVERSITY OF EDINBURGH MEDICAL SCHOOL

Admissions Office
Faculty of Medicine Office
Medical School
Teviot Place
Edinburgh EH8 9AG

UCAS code: EDINB E56 A100 MBChB/Med5 (5 years)
              EDINB E56 A104 MBChB/Med6 (6 years)

☎   (0131) 650 3187 – Admissions Office
Fax: (0131) 650 6525 – Admissions Office
WWW: http://www.ed.ac.uk

Medical teaching has been conducted in Edinburgh since the 1500s and the
Faculty of Medicine was established in 1727. Edinburgh is currently home of
the Royal Medical Society, the oldest student medical society in the UK.

COURSE OUTLINE

A one-year premedical course
(A104) is available for applicants
who do not have the necessary
science qualifications to enter the
medical course directly. Two
students were accepted on to A104
from 439 applicants in 1994–5.

The medical course (A100) lasts
five years and is divided into three
phases. **Phase I** lasts for two years,
starting with a one-term integrated
introductory course in medical
biology. This is followed by two
terms of more detailed teaching in
anatomy, biochemistry and
physiology. The second year
includes teaching in endocrinology,
neuroscience, pharmacology,
microbiology and pathology.
Behavioural sciences and clinical
correlation are taught throughout
Phase I. The sixth term includes
options for further study.

Phase II occupies Year 3 and is
a systems-based introductory clinical
year which commences clinical
teaching. Students spend every
morning on the wards. An
introductory course is followed by a
series of rotations. **Phase III** lasts

96 weeks and contains three
holidays of two weeks each. There
are a succession of full-time
attachments to wards in small
groups, or individually to general
practices. There are very few
lectures during this phase.
Attachments are held both in
Edinburgh and adjacent districts.

ASSESSMENT

Continuous assessment and/or a
contribution from class examinations
is used by some departments.
'Traditional' end of course
examinations are held, with
multiple-choice and written papers.

INTERCALATED DEGREE

Selected students can undertake a
BSc (Medical Sciences) Honours
degree at the end of Phase I or
later. This option is taken by about
80 students a year.

ELECTIVE PERIOD

A 16-week elective period is taken
in Phase III and can be spent in
Edinburgh, elsewhere in the UK, or
abroad. Attachments have to be
approved by the Director of Studies.

AT A GLANCE

Applications received	**2308 (A100)**
Offers made	**437 (A100)**
Total accepted	**201 (A100)**
Overseas accepted	**13 (A100)**
Interview	**No**
Typical A level offer	**AAB**
Typical SCE Highers offer	**AAAAB**
Premedical course	**Yes**
Length of course	**5 years***
Degrees	**MB ChB**
Intercalated degree	**BSc (MedSci) (optional)**
Elective period	**16 weeks**

(*6 years if premedical course taken)

ENTRY REQUIREMENTS

- 3 A levels **must** include Chemistry and two of Biology, Mathematics and Physics; **or** Chemistry and Biology and one other approved A level (A grade must be in a science)

- 2 AS levels (at grade B) can be offered with A level Chemistry and Biology (at grade A)

- 5 SCE Highers must include Chemistry and normally two of Biology, Mathematics or Physics

- SCE S grade (grade 3) or GCSE (grade C) or equivalent, in English, a foreign language, Biology and Mathematics

- Dual Award Combined Sciences (two B grades) may be offered instead of GCSE grades in sciences

- Biology may be offered as SCOTVEC modules instead of SCE S grade

FURTHER INFORMATION

Applicants are welcome to visit the medical school. Visits should be arranged by letter or telephone to the Admissions Office. An alternative prospectus is available by sending £1.00 to: Edinburgh University Students' Association, Bristol Square, Edinburgh EH8 9AL.

A limited number of applicants can apply for deferred entry and are expected to indicate their intentions for the year out.

LIVING IN EDINBURGH

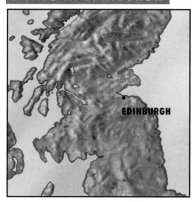

Edinburgh is the capital city of Scotland and has a population of half a million. The well-known Edinburgh Festival is only one of its cultural attractions, the city also boasting several museums, galleries and concert halls.

Edinburgh has good links with other towns and cities, including its own airport. The local countryside is also easily accessible although the city itself has many parks and gardens.

The University Students' Association offers a wide range of services. In addition, students also become members of the Sports Union, with access to a number of sports facilities.

UNIVERSITY OF EDINBURGH MEDICAL SCHOOL

UNIVERSITY OF GLASGOW MEDICAL SCHOOL

Admissions Committee Administrator
Medical Faculty Office
University of Glasgow
Glasgow G12 8QQ

UCAS code: GLASG G28 A100 MB/ChB

☎   (0141) 330 4424 – Admissions enquires
       (0141) 330 4239 – General enquires
WWW: http://www.gla.ac.uk

The training of doctors began in Glasgow almost 400 years ago and the medical school is now one of Europe's largest. Glasgow's rapid expansion between the mid-nineteenth and mid-twentieth centuries created social problems which led to a particular interest in preventative medicine.

COURSE OUTLINE

A new medical curriculum was introduced in 1996. Lasting five years, it is organised into a series of themes with a clinical approach from Year 1. The themes include: Clinical method, practical skills and patient care; Communication skills; Human biology; Human disease; Man in society/ethics; Public health; Handicap, disability and rehabilitation; Finding out, research and experiment; Multicultural medicine.

The traditional division between preclinical and clinical teaching no longer exists and there is much less emphasis on lectures. Instead, learning is based around group work and resource-based individual work, in addition to project work and student-centred learning.

The curriculum is based around four main components, in line with the recommendations of *Tomorrow's Doctors*. **The core** presents an integrated and comprehensive overview of medical and scientific principles. **Special study modules** account for around 20% of the course, allowing the detailed study of subjects of particular interest. **Vocational studies** encourage patient contact and are followed by the **clinical core** based around small group work in hospitals and the community.

INTERCALATED DEGREE

A one-year Honours BSc (MedSci) is available in the Medical Faculty at the end of Year 3. Alternatively, some students may be invited to undertake a two-year BSc with Honours in the Faculty of Science after Year 2.

ELECTIVE PERIOD

Two separate elective periods are undertaken, both four weeks in length. The first period is taken between Years 3 and 4, and the second between Years 4 and 5, and can be spent in the UK or abroad.

AT A GLANCE

Applications received	**1844**
Offers made	**574**
Total accepted	**225**
Overseas accepted	**22**
Interview	**Yes**
Typical A level offer	**AAB**
Typical SCE Highers offer	**AAAAB**
Premedical course	**No**
Length of course	**5 years**
Degrees	**MB ChB**
Intercalated degree	**BSc (optional)**
Elective period	**2 × 4 weeks**

LIVING IN GLASGOW

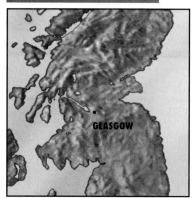

GLASGOW

Glasgow is Scotland's largest city and has a full-time student population of over 15,000. The city offers a wide variety of music and arts, and has taken increasing pride in its culture over the last few years. In 1990 it was the Cultural Capital of Europe and will be the European City of Architecture & Design in 1999.

The University has two students' unions (Glasgow University Union and Queen Margaret Union) and numerous students' clubs and societies offering a full range of recreational activities. All the students' societies cooperate in the running of the annual Freshers' Week, an event to welcome new students.

ENTRY REQUIREMENTS

- 3 A levels **or** 5 SCE Highers

- A levels **must** include Chemistry and one from Biology, Mathematics or Physics

- 2 AS levels are equivalent to one A level

- SCE Highers **must** include Chemistry and two from Biology (or Human Biology), Mathematics or Physics

- pass in English at GCSE or Standard Grade 1, 2, 3

- GCSE passes are recommended in Biology, Mathematics and Physics if not studied at A level

FURTHER INFORMATION

Interviews are held from November until March and offers are made from January/February.

An annual Open Day is held (on Wednesday, 24 September, in 1997). In addition, a videotape (*Glasgow University: A Rough Guide*) can be borrowed free of charge. For more information, contact the Schools & Colleges Liaison Service at the University of Glasgow, Glasgow G12 8QQ, ☎ (0141) 330 4263.

UNIVERSITY OF LEEDS MEDICAL SCHOOL

The Admissions Office
School of Medicine
Room 7.10, Level 7
Worsley Medical and Dental Building
University of Leeds
Leeds LS2 9JT

UCAS code: LEEDS L23 A100 MBChB

☎   (0113) 233 4362 – Admissions enquiries
Fax: (0113) 233 4375
WWW: http://www.leeds.ac.uk

The Leeds Faculty of Medicine and Dentistry is one of the UK's largest centres of medical and dental teaching and research. Most preclinical teaching takes place at the Worsley Medical and Dental Building, opened in 1979. Clinical teaching takes place at the Leeds General Infirmary, St James's University Hospital and other hospitals and general practices around the region.

COURSE OUTLINE

A new curriculum was introduced for the five-year course in 1992 and is still undergoing changes. Although the course is broadly divided into a two-year preclinical and a three-year clinical course, the two are becoming increasingly integrated.

In **Years 1 and 2**, basic sciences teaching is combined with courses in behavioural sciences, communication skills, information technology, medical statistics and public health. Clinical science symposia are used to place the teaching in a clinical context and a literature review project is undertaken. **Year 3** introduces daily patient contact after a basic clinical skills introductory course. In between clinical attachments there is a block of teaching in laboratory and scientific medicine. A four-week special study module is undertaken at the end of Year 3. During **Year 4** students train in the medical and surgical specialties. Residential attachments take place around the region. An elective period in **Year 5** is followed by further training in medicine and surgery, with a choice of optional specialties.

ASSESSMENT

Main examinations are held at the end of subject teaching, taking into account earlier class examinations in these subjects. The final qualifying examination comprises examinations in psychiatry, paediatrics and child health, obstetrics & gynaecology, and medicine and surgery. These take place after the subject teaching in Years 4 and 5 and include written and clinical examinations.

INTERCALATED DEGREE

Students who achieve high standards may take a BSc Honours degree in one of the medical sciences at the end of Year 2 or 3. Rarely, students may be able to intercalate a PhD.

ELECTIVE PERIOD

A ten-week elective period is held at the start of Year 5. The school has three ERASMUS links, in France, Italy and Spain.

AT A GLANCE

Applications received	**2838**
Offers made	**663**
Total accepted	**202**
Overseas accepted	**15**
Interview	**Yes**
Typical A level offer	**ABB**
Premedical course	**No**
Length of course	**5 years**
Degrees	**MB ChB**
Intercalated degree	**BSc (optional)**
Elective period	**10 weeks**

ENTRY REQUIREMENTS

- 3 A levels or their equivalent

- **must** include A or AS level Chemistry

- no restriction on other subjects as long as they have a sufficient academic base and at least one is a full A level

- GCSE grade B minimum in two of Biology, Mathematics and Physics if not offered at A level

- a substantial number of GCSE passes, at a high standard, in a broad range of subjects

- GCSE English (grade C) or equivalent

FURTHER INFORMATION

Between 15 and 20 places are set aside each year for mature students and graduates. Competition is intense. Deferred entry is encouraged for those wishing to gain experience of work, voluntary service or travel.

General university open days are held in late spring and early summer. Contact the Admissions Office (address on previous page) or: Schools Liaison Office, Central Administration, University of Leeds, Leeds LS2 9JT, ☎ (0113) 233 3996. Individual visits cannot be arranged. For a copy of the Student Union Handbook and Alternative Prospectus, ☎ (0113) 243 9071.

LIVING IN LEEDS

In recent years Leeds has been rejuvenated to become a prosperous and bustling city with a particularly strong Arts scene. The city is home to Opera North, and the City Art Gallery is one of the best outside London. On the sports front, Headingley is home to Yorkshire Country Cricket Club and Leeds United can be found at Elland Road.

The University has 20,000 degree students and therefore offers a diverse range of recreational activities. Further afield, the Yorkshire Dales, North York Moors and Pennines all provide ample opportunity for outdoor pursuits. The city has good road and rail links with the rest of the UK, and Leeds/Bradford Airport is close at hand.

UNIVERSITY OF LEEDS MEDICAL SCHOOL

UNIVERSITY OF LEICESTER MEDICAL SCHOOL

Admissions Office
Leicester University
University Road
Leicester LE1 7RH

UCAS code: LEICR L34 A100 MBChB

☎   (0116) 252 2969 – General enquiries
    (0116) 252 2966 – Admissions Tutor
Fax: (0116) 252 3013
WWW: http://www.le.ac.uk

Medical teaching in Leicester is centred around three major hospitals: Leicester Royal Infirmary, Glenfield General Hospital and Leicester General Hospital.

COURSE OUTLINE

Leicester medical school implemented a new curriculum in 1994, in line with *Tomorrow's Doctors*. The medical course is divided into two phases, with clinical teaching forming a significant component of both.

Phase I runs over five semesters, with six modules per semester. A core of material, taken by all students, comprises 26 modules. Special study modules, during which students can choose which topics to study, comprise the remainder. During Year 1 the emphasis is on gaining clinical and communication skills, followed by a hospital-based introductory course in Year 2. Medical sciences are taught throughout in an integrated manner, and a strong emphasis is placed upon social and behavioural medicine.

Phase II aims to develop students' skills with a series of relatively long clinical attachments in small clinical teaching groups.

ASSESSMENT

The Phase I core module is assessed continuously, while a variety of methods are used to assess the special study modules. During Phase II, students compile a 'case portfolio' and are examined on their clinical skills by a variety of methods. In all parts of the course distinction or merit can be earned. The MB ChB degree may be awarded with honours if the necessary number of distinctions and merits have been obtained. Following the final clinical examinations, a time of 'Additional Clinical Practice' is spent shadowing the house officer in the post that the student will take over the following August.

INTERCALATED DEGREE

About 10% of students undertake an intercalated BSc Honours degree. A very small number may go on to the BSc MB PhD programme.

ELECTIVE PERIOD

The elective period occupies one block during Phase II. More than 80% of students go abroad, and some financial assistance may be available. Students make a report of their experiences to the Faculty on their return.

AT A GLANCE

Applications received	**2096**
Offers made	**511**
Total accepted	**155**
Overseas accepted	**13**
Interview	**Yes**
Typical A level offer	**ABB**
Premedical course	**No**
Length of course	**5 years**
Degrees	**MB ChB**
Intercalated degree	**BSc (optional)**
Elective period	**One block (Phase II)**

ENTRY REQUIREMENTS

- 3 A levels **or** 2 A + 2 AS levels

- **must** include A level Chemistry, one other science A level and a third A level in a science, arts or social science subject (**not** General Studies)

- GCSE English Language and sciences if not held at A or AS level

FURTHER INFORMATION

Applications are welcomed from those with International or European Baccalaureate, BTEC and overseas qualifications. Advanced GNVQ qualifications are considered with A level Chemistry.

New undergraduates are guaranteed a place in university accommodation, subject to meeting offer/place acceptance deadlines.

The medical school holds an annual Open Day, usually in April. A 20-minute videotape about the University (*Climb to Success*) is available for loan. For further details, contact the Schools & Colleges Liaison Officer, ☎ (0116) 252 2674, Fax (0116) 252 2447, or by E-mail at admissions@le.ac.uk.

UNIVERSITY OF LEICESTER MEDICAL SCHOOL

'If you're thinking of applying to Leicester, go for it! Our course may have the occasional teething problem, but meeting patients in the first year and starting on the wards in the second year is fantastic — most of the work we do is clinically oriented. I can't think of a friendlier place.'

'Of the new courses designed as a result of the GMC's report Tomorrow's Doctors, I think Leicester's course appears to be one of the better ones and is popular with the students on it.'

UNIVERSITY OF LIVERPOOL MEDICAL SCHOOL
Faculty of Medicine
The University of Liverpool
PO Box 147
Liverpool L69 3BX

UCAS code: LVRPL L41 A100 MBChB

☎   (0151) 709 7172 – Admissions Secretary
Fax: (0151) 708 6502
WWW: http://www.liv.ac.uk

Liverpool's medical school was established in 1834 and the city was the site of the country's first hospital X-ray department in 1896. The well-known Liverpool School of Tropical Medicine was founded in 1898.

COURSE OUTLINE
A new medical course was introduced in 1996 and follows the recommendations in *Tomorrow's Doctors*. It is divided into three phases.

The foundations of clinical practice are laid in **Phase 1**, which lasts for one year. Halfway through the year, the first four-week special study module allows students to study a basic science topic in more detail.

Phase 2 lasts three years and is divided into three *Clinical Practice* sections. Clinical Practice 1 lasts 24 weeks, during which students work in hospitals and the community. Clinical Practice 2 lasts 20 weeks, during which students work with medical and surgical teams in hospitals throughout the region, as well as spending time with GPs. Clinical Practice 3 comprises three 16-week rotations concerned with the management of illness and disease.

Phase 3 is the final year and is an *Intensive Clinical Experience*. Students undertake three 12-week rotations in a peripheral hospital, a community health team and a 'career' elective.

ASSESSMENT
There are both formal and informal assessments during the course. Formal assessment takes place at the end of each semester. Theoretical assessments are completed with an examination at the end of Year 4 (Phase 2). Final examinations at the end of Year 5 (Phase 3) are clinically oriented.

INTERCALATED DEGREE
After studying a subject in depth during a special study module, students can choose to undertake an additional year of further study, for which some scholarships are available. This can lead to an intercalated degree in a science subject. Students can also opt to study a Bachelor of Clinical Science degree.

ELECTIVE PERIOD
A 12-week elective period is taken in between Clinical Practice 2 and Clinical Practice 3, and many electives are undertaken overseas. Travelling scholarships are available for this purpose.

AT A GLANCE

Applications received	**1603**
Offers made	**713**
Total accepted	**176**
Overseas accepted	**14**
Interview	**Yes**
Typical A level offer	**ABB**
Premedical course	**No**
Length of course	**5 years**
Degrees	**MB ChB**
Intercalated degree	**Optional**
Elective period	**12 weeks**

ENTRY REQUIREMENTS

- 3 A levels or 2 A + 2 AS levels

- if 3 A levels are offered, one must be Chemistry, plus one of Biology (or Zoology), Mathematics or Physics, plus one subject with at least 60% academic content

- for acceptable A + AS level combinations, consult the prospectus

- if not offering Biology (or Zoology) or Physics (or Physics with Mathematics) at A or AS level, evidence of knowledge of these subjects at GCSE level must be produced

- 6 GCSE subjects at grade A or B (including English and Mathematics)

FURTHER INFORMATION

An alternative prospectus looking at student life in Liverpool can be obtained by sending a cheque or postal order for £2.00 (payable to *Liverpool University Guild of Students*) to: Schools Liaison Officer, The Guild of Students, 160 Mount Pleasant, Liverpool L69 7BR.

An annual open day is organised, usually in May. Separate visits may also be arranged. Contact: Schools and Colleges Liaison, The University of Liverpool, Liverpool L69 3BX or ☎ (0151) 794 5927.

LIVING IN LIVERPOOL

The seaport city of Liverpool is well-known for its football and its music. It also has some excellent Arts facilities, including the Walker and Liverpool Tate galleries. Liverpool is increasingly renowned for its lively nightlife and has a huge range of pubs (many of which open late) and clubs.

Further afield are the cities of Chester and Manchester, together with the outdoor activities available in Cumbria and North Wales. London is less than three hours' away by rail.

The University has 12,000 full-time students and its Guild of Students (the union) has excellent recently-renovated facilities which range from a launderette and stationery shop to a travel agency and advice centre.

UNIVERSITY OF LIVERPOOL MEDICAL SCHOOL

IMPERIAL COLLEGE SCHOOL OF MEDICINE

School of Medicine Admissions
Imperial College
London SW7 2AZ

UCAS code: IMP I50 A100 Medicine

☎ (0171) 594 3598
Fax: (0171) 594 3599
E-mail: admitmed@ic.ac.uk
WWW: http://www.ic.ac.uk

At the time of writing, the final stages in the formation of the Imperial College School of Medicine (ICSM) were taking place. The new institution unites Imperial College School of Medicine at St Mary's with the National Heart and Lung Institute, Charing Cross & Westminster Medical School and the Royal Postgraduate Medical School. As the first student intake into the new medical school is in 1998, the information given in this section is subject to change.

COURSE OUTLINE

Students joining the course in 1998 will follow a new six-year curriculum that includes one year devoted to a modular BSc degree. Teaching for this course will be based in a new Biomedical Sciences Building, due to open in 1998.

In accordance with the *Tomorrow's Doctors* recommendations, the new course will provide an integrated approach to basic medical, pathological and clinical sciences and will have an emphasis on clinical relevance. Following a short Foundation Course, the MB BS curriculum consists of three main elements: Systems and Topics, Doctor and Patient, and Clinical Experience.

Systems and Topics courses will be taught during five years of the six-year curriculum, although the amount of time allotted to this teaching gradually falls. Teaching methods will include lectures, practicals, seminars and tutorials. The **Doctor and Patient** course also runs throughout the MB BS course for an average of one day per week, based at all the hospitals associated with ICSM. **Clinical Experience** will place students in direct contact with patients from Year 1, and the time allocated will increase during the course.

ASSESSMENT

It is expected that assessment methods will reflect the integrated structure of the new medical course, with a significant amount of in-course assessment. This will reduce the workload associated with final examinations.

INTERCALATED DEGREE

All students will study for a BSc degree through a modular programme, choosing 16 three-week modules from a wide variety of options.

ELECTIVE PERIOD

An eight-week elective period is available during the final phase of the course for students to work in a medical field of their own choice in the UK or abroad.

AT A GLANCE

Applications received	**Not yet known**
Offers made	**Not yet known**
Places available	**286**
Overseas places	**Not yet known**
Interview	**Yes**
Typical A level offer	**ABB**
Premedical course	**No**
Length of course	**6 years**
Degrees	**MB BS**
Intercalated degree	**BSc (compulsory)**
Elective period	**8 weeks**

ENTRY REQUIREMENTS

- 3 A levels **or** 2 A + 2 AS levels

- **must** include Chemistry at A or AS level (overseas students may offer Physical Science in place of Chemistry)

- A or AS level Biology is not essential but highly recommended

- GCSE English Language, Biology (or Human Biology), Physics and Mathematics (or Additional Mathematics or Statistics) at grade B or above if not held at A or AS level

- check the prospectus for details of other acceptable examinations, combinations and substitutions

FURTHER INFORMATION

Up to 25 places may be offered to mature or graduate applicants. Graduates should normally have at least a 2:1 Honours degree.

A second competitive interview is held in March or April for candidates shortlisted for scholarships on the basis of their initial interview performance. Some scholarships are also awarded on the basis of examination results at the time of entry to the medical school.

For information about Open Days or informal visits contact School Liaison Office, Room 321, Sherfield Building, Imperial College, London SW7 2AZ.

LIVING NEAR ICSM

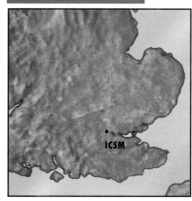

ICSM

The main Imperial College campus is located in South Kensington, placing it within easy reach of all the social, sporting and cultural activities that London has to offer. There are numerous clubs and societies, and the college has access to several outdoor sports facilities, including a boathouse on the Thames at Putney.

An alternative prospectus, describing life at the college from the students' perspective, can be obtained from Imperial College Union (☎ (0171) 594 8060).

Students also become members of the University of London Union (ULU). The ULU site in Malet Street has excellent facilities, including an entertainment complex. The ULU also has extensive indoor and outdoor sports facilities.

IMPERIAL COLLEGE SCHOOL OF MEDICINE

KING'S COLLEGE SCHOOL OF MEDICINE & DENTISTRY

KING'S COLLEGE SCHOOL OF MEDICINE & DENTISTRY

The Assistant Registrar
King's College School of Medicine & Dentistry
Bessemer Road
London SE5 9PJ

UCAS code: KCSMD K72 A100 MBBS (5 years)
KCSMD K72 A103 MBBS/f (6 years)

☎ (0171) 737 4000 ext. 4017 – Application enquiries
WWW: http://www.kcl.ac.uk

King's is one of the oldest colleges of the University of London, and the medical school was established in 1831. King's College London has agreed in principle to a merger with UMDS (see page 56), although a definite date was not available at the time of writing.

COURSE OUTLINE

A Foundation Course in Natural Sciences (A103) is available for those without the necessary science qualifications to prepare for the medical course, and lasts one year. Ten students were accepted on to A103 from 326 applicants in 1994–5.

The main MB BS course (A100) has a new curriculum that was introduced in 1996. It is based upon five themes or 'strands': Cells & Molecules, Systems, Practice of Medicine, Professional Skills and Special Study Modules. Teaching is based on lectures, small groups, practicals and tutorials, together with clinical bedside teaching.

A five-week foundation course takes place at the start of **Year 1**, followed mostly by the Systems strand (although elements of the other four strands are included). **Year 2** continues this strand but more time is spent on Practice of Medicine. **Years 3 and 4** both last 46 weeks and the emphasis moves further towards the Practice of Medicine strand, with a greater degree of clinical teaching. **Year 5** consists of clinical attachments in medicine, surgery, general practice, obstetrics & gynaecology, and child health. There are also opportunities for students to choose their own attachments.

ASSESSMENT

Examinations are held at the end of each year and marks contribute to the final result. Continuous assessment accounts for up to 40% of the marks. Special study modules and elective periods are also assessed. There are no major written examinations in Year 5 and assessments concentrate on skills, attitudes and expertise in patient management.

INTERCALATED DEGREE

Students are encouraged to take a one-year intercalated BSc if they wish to do so. In 1995–6 there were 45 places available. Intercalation usually occurs at the end of Year 2, but can be taken at the end of Years 3 or 4. A wide choice of courses is available. Eight MRC scholarships are currently available and other sources of funding may also be obtainable.

ELECTIVE PERIOD

There are two elective periods, both in Year 5. One is science-based and the other primarily clinical. The clinical elective is often taken abroad.

AT A GLANCE

Applications received	**2324 (A100)**
Offers made	**382 (A100)**
Total accepted	**115 (A100)**
Overseas accepted	**5 (A100)**
Interview	**Yes**
Typical A level offer	**ABB**
Premedical course	**Yes**
Length of course	**5 years***
Degrees	**MB BS**
Intercalated degree	**BSc (optional)**
Elective period	**2 (clinical & scientific)**

*(*6 years if Foundation Course taken)*

ENTRY REQUIREMENTS

- 3 A levels **or** 2 A + 2 AS levels

- **must** include A or AS level Chemistry

- numerous subject combinations are available – consult the prospectus for further information

- students not meeting entry requirements should seek advice from: University of London Entry Requirements Department, Senate House, Malet Street, London WC1E 7HU

FURTHER INFORMATION

King's College London holds an annual Open Day for prospective applicants. For further information, contact: Student Recruitment & Exchanges Office, Cornwall House, King's College London, Waterloo Road, London SE1 8WA. This office also arranges tours of the basic sciences teaching department five times a year. A full tour of the college and hospital are available at the time of interview.

LIVING NEAR KCSMD

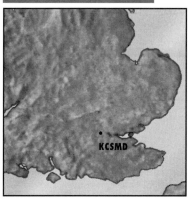

Medical students at KCSMD spend most of their time at one of the college's two campuses. Basic medical science teaching takes place at the Strand campus, which is located in the centre of London. Clinical teaching takes place at the Denmark Hill campus near Ruskin Park. The Students' Union building overlooks the Thames and offers such facilities as a café bar and shopping mall.

There are two sports grounds – one at New Malden, and the other near to the Denmark Hill campus. The Denmark Hill campus also has a Guild of Students which offers a range of social and sporting events, together with over 30 clubs and societies.

KING'S COLLEGE SCHOOL OF MEDICINE & DENTISTRY

THE ROYAL FREE HOSPITAL SCHOOL OF MEDICINE

THE ROYAL FREE HOSPITAL SCHOOL OF MEDICINE
The Registrar
Royal Free Hospital
School of Medicine
Rowland Hill Street
London NW3 2PF

UCAS code: RFHSM R60 A100 MBBS

☎   (0171) 794 0500 ext. 4271
        (0171) 830 2686
WWW: http://www.rfhsm.ac.uk

The Royal Free Hospital was founded in 1837 to provide free care for the sick.
It is likely that the Medical School will merge with the University College
London Medical School in 1998 or 1999 to form the Royal Free and
University College Medical School, with an annual intake of around 330
students.

COURSE OUTLINE
The five-year course is divided into
two periods. The first six terms are
devoted to the study of basic
medical sciences, general pathology
and pharmacology. Clinical lectures
and demonstrations take place
during each term to emphasise
clinical relevance. There is also a
family attachment programme,
called *The Family Study*, in which
students are linked with a local
family via a GP.

The clinical course is primarily
based in the Royal Free Hospital.
Additional experience will be
gained in other district hospitals.
The course begins with a three-week
Introductory Course, followed by
eight six-week attachments to firms
in the basic medical and surgical
disciplines. There is then a five-week
pathology and special subjects
block. More specialised attachments
follow in Year 4, and students
spend about 25% of their time away
from the Royal Free Hospital. Year 5
contains an elective period as well
as senior student 'apprenticeships'.

ASSESSMENT
Examinations are held at the end of
the relevant course for the subjects
studied in Years 1 and 2. This
comprises a Part I examination in
Year 1, and Parts II–IV in Year 2.
Students must pass Part I before
proceeding to Year 2, and Parts
II–IV before starting the Clinical
Studies course. Clinical
examinations consist of assessment
tests held in the relevant year of the
course, leading to the Part V
examinations at the end of Year 5.

INTERCALATED DEGREE
Students with good passes in the
Parts I–IV examinations are
encouraged to consider taking an
intercalated BSc degree, lasting
three terms. Almost half the students
currently do so, most at the Royal
Free but some elsewhere in the
University of London.

ELECTIVE PERIOD
An eight-week elective period takes
place in Year 5. Students can work
in a suitable institution or hospital
anywhere in the world. A number of
elective scholarships are available.

AT A GLANCE

Applications received	**1610**
Offers made	**293**
Total accepted	**105**
Overseas accepted	**7**
Interview	**Yes**
Typical A level offer	**BBB**
Premedical course	**No**
Length of course	**5 years**
Degrees	**MB BS**
Intercalated degree	**BSc (optional)**
Elective period	**8 weeks**

LIVING NEAR THE ROYAL FREE

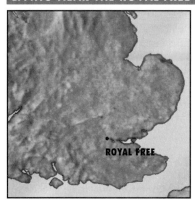

ROYAL FREE

ENTRY REQUIREMENTS

- 3 A levels **or** 2 A + 2 AS levels

- Chemistry is required at A level

- the preferred combination is Chemistry and a Biological subject with either Physics or Mathematics

- several other combinations are acceptable – see prospectus for details

- good GCSE/O level passes in English Language and Mathematics are required

FURTHER INFORMATION

Accommodation is available for 78 students, with priority given to those in their first year. Clinical students have access to 16 study bedrooms managed by a charitable trust. Halls of residence of the University of London are also available to students and are situated in Bloomsbury.

For further information about entry to the medical school contact The Registrar at the address given on the previous page.

One of the Royal Free's strengths is the medical school sharing the same site as the hospital. This leads to a greater mixing between students in different years of the course than often occurs elsewhere. This is also encouraged by the 'Uncle and Aunty' scheme, in which new students are allocated to one in the year above who helps them settle into the course.

The Students' Union is affiliated to the University of London Union (ULU) and organises a variety of sporting and social events. The hospital has its own recreation centre which includes a swimming pool and gymnasium, and also has access to an athletics ground in Enfield.

THE ROYAL FREE HOSPITAL SCHOOL OF MEDICINE

ST BARTHOLOMEW'S AND THE ROYAL LONDON SCHOOL OF MEDICINE AND DENTISTRY

The Admissions Office
St Bartholomew's and the Royal London School
of Medicine and Dentistry
Queen Mary and Westfield College
Turner Street
London E1 2AD

UCAS code: QMW Q50 A100 W MBBS

☎ (0171) 377 7611
Fax: (0171) 377 7677
WWW: http://www.mds.qmw.ac.uk

The medical colleges of St Bartholomew's Hospital and the Royal London Hospital merged in 1995 to create St Bartholomew's and the Royal London School of Medicine and Dentistry at Queen Mary and Westfield College. Admissions figures were not available at the time of writing, but it was anticipated that 202 places would be available in 1997.

COURSE OUTLINE

The medical curriculum was introduced in 1990 and anticipated many of the recommendations in *Tomorrow's Doctors*. The course is divided into three phases.

Phase I forms the integrated, systems-based basic medical sciences course, which lasts for five terms. There is also a community-based module and regular clinical demonstrations. **Phase II** covers such topics as human sciences, biometry, ethics, clinical and communication skills and community dental health, and lasts for two terms. It is designed as a transition between the basic medical sciences and clinical training.

Phase III lasts eight terms, beginning with a course in clinical and pathological processes, followed by attachments in medicine and surgery. A block of clinico-pathological teaching ends Year 3. Year 4 covers the major specialties in rotation, and Year 5 begins with the final block of clinical-pathological teaching, followed by further rotations. In addition, there are three four-week special study modules and an eight-week elective.

ASSESSMENT

During Phase I, each module contains some in-course assessment, although there are also two main examinations. Phase II is assessed by a mix of formal examinations and 'workbook assignment'. Apart from pathology, which is examined in November of Year 5, all the clinical subjects are examined in June of Year 5, by five written papers and a clinical examination.

INTERCALATED DEGREE

Around 70–80 students take a one-year intercalated degree. After term five, students can opt to take a BSc degree. Alternatively, students can undertake a one-year BMedSci degree after Year 4.

ELECTIVE PERIOD

An eight-week elective period is available during Year 5 of the course.

AT A GLANCE

Applications received	**Not known**
Offers made	**Not known**
Places available	**202 (1997)**
Overseas accepted	**Not known**
Interview	**Yes**
Typical A level offer	**BBB**
Premedical course	**No**
Length of course	**5 years**
Degrees	**MB BS**
Intercalated degree	**BSc or BMedSci (optional)**
Elective period	**8 weeks**

ENTRY REQUIREMENTS

- 3 A levels **or** 2 A + 2 AS levels

- **must** include A level Chemistry

- the second A level (or two AS levels) needs to be Biology, Mathematics or Physics

- the third A level (or two AS levels) can be almost any other academic subject

- GCSE pass in English Language

- GCSE Biology if not offered at A level

- consult the prospectus for alternative subjects and combinations which may be acceptable

FURTHER INFORMATION

Applications for deferred entry are welcomed with constructive plans for the year off.

Mature and graduate students make up 15% of the student body. The normal upper age limit is 30 years. Applications from high-calibre graduates (with at least an upper second class degree) are welcomed.

For further information about the medical course, admissions, campus tours and open days, contact the Admissions Office at the address given on the previous page.

LIVING NEAR QMW COLLEGE

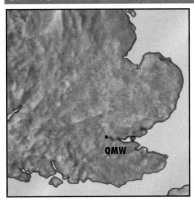

Medical students at St Bartholomew's and the Royal London School of Medicine are based around the East End and City of London, placing them within easy reach of many of the amenities that the capital has to offer. Compared to the rest of London, living in the East End is relatively inexpensive.

There is an Association of Medical and Dental Students which supports over 30 clubs and societies covering a wide range of interests. There are good facilities available at both major hospital sites, including bookshops, social and sporting facilities. Further afield there is a sports ground and a boat club. QMW College has its own students' union and students can also use the University of London Union's facilities.

ST BARTHOLOMEW'S AND THE ROYAL LONDON SCHOOL OF MEDICINE AND DENTISTRY

ST GEORGE'S HOSPITAL MEDICAL SCHOOL

Admissions Officer
St George's Hospital Medical School
Cranmer Terrace
London SW17 0RE

UCAS code: SGEO S49 A100 MBBS

☎   (0181) 725 5992 – Admissions Officer
Fax: (0181) 725 3426
WWW: http://www.sghms.ac.uk

St George's Medical School moved into new buildings in Tooting in 1976 to become the only medical school in the South West Thames Region. The medical school shares its campus with the new St George's Hospital and is London's largest single medical school, with around 160 first-year admissions annually.

COURSE OUTLINE

A new medical curriculum was introduced in 1996, taking an integrated approach to teaching. A number of special study modules, allowing students to study chosen areas in greater depth, are available from Year 2 onwards.

Years 1 and 2 are organised into six ten-week terms, commencing with a Foundation Module to introduce students to basic 'core' concepts. Following this, the traditional subjects are taught in an integrated way as a series of systems-based modules with a clinical emphasis.

Years 3 and 4 are each divided into three terms of approximately 15 weeks, with much of the time being based around clinical firms. Teaching is based around both body-system modules (e.g. 'alimentary') and non-system modules (e.g. oncology). A Senior Clinical Experience module is undertaken at the end of Year 4.

Most of **Year 5** is spent away from St George's and is a chance to gain further clinical experience and improve clinical skills. The year includes two 'shadow' house officer appointments in medicine and surgery.

ASSESSMENT

Continuous assessment is a feature of the whole course, with a variety of assessment methods. Short written or practical examinations are held at the end of each term, together (possibly) with some in-course assessment. A synoptic examination is held at the end of most years.

INTERCALATED DEGREE

Selected students can spend an additional year (between Years 2 and 3) undertaking a BSc Honours degree in basic medical sciences, based at St George's or elsewhere in the University of London. Up to eight students may undertake a BSc in clinical sciences between Years 4 and 5.

ELECTIVE PERIOD

Students may undertake a nine-week elective period during Year 5. Alternatively, they may opt for another special study module at St George's.

AT A GLANCE

Applications received	**2880**
Offers made	**319**
Total accepted	**157**
Overseas accepted	**8**
Interview	**Yes**
Typical A level offer	**ABB**
Premedical course	**No**
Length of course	**5 years**
Degrees	**MB BS**
Intercalated degree	**BSc (optional)**
Elective period	**9 weeks**

ENTRY REQUIREMENTS

- 3 A levels **or** 2 A + 2 AS levels

- **must** include either Biology or Chemistry at A level

- if Biology is offered at A level, Chemistry must be offered at A or AS level

- GCSE Biology, Mathematics and Physics (or two combined or integrated science subjects in place of any one of these) at grade C or above unless offered at A or AS level

- GCSE Human Biology can be offered instead of Biology, and Additional Mathematics or Statistics instead of Mathematics

- GCSE English Language at grade B or better

- candidates without A or AS level Biology may be required to undertake a short course before starting the MB BS course

FURTHER INFORMATION

Informal tours of the medical school are organised and dates are available from the Admissions Officer. Tours commence with a video (Why St George's?) and last around 90 minutes.

Candidates can apply to defer entry for a year, and the medical school is looking into the provision of some bursaries for those with particularly interesting plans.

LIVING NEAR ST GEORGE'S

ST. GEORGE'S

St George's is the only medical school in the South West Thames Region. New undergraduates are offered a self-catering study bedroom in a private estate of terraced houses within a mile of the medical school.

There are good outdoor sports facilities at Cobham (Surrey) and a boathouse on the Thames. There is also an indoor sports complex on the hospital site.

The medical student society, the School Club, organises many social events, including an annual ball, and there are a number of societies covering a wide range of interests.

'St George's is a really friendly medical school and an excellent choice.'

'With the new modular courses at St George's, involving more self-directed learning, self-discipline is essential. You have to keep on top of your work!'

ST GEORGE'S HOSPITAL MEDICAL SCHOOL

UNITED MEDICAL AND DENTAL SCHOOLS OF GUY'S AND ST THOMAS'S HOSPITALS

UNITED MEDICAL AND DENTAL SCHOOLS OF GUY'S AND ST THOMAS'S HOSPITALS

Admissions Officer
United Medical & Dental Schools
St Thomas's Hospital
Lambeth Palace Road
London SE1 7EH

UCAS code: UMDS U60 A100 MBBS

☎   (0171) 922 8013
Fax: (0171) 928 0069
WWW: http://www.umds.ac.uk

The Medical and Dental Schools of Guy's and St Thomas's Hospitals merged in the early 1980s to form UMDS. Plans exist for the eventual merger of UMDS with King's College School of Medicine and Dentistry.

COURSE OUTLINE

The medical curriculum at UMDS has been revised in line with the recommendations in *Tomorrow's Doctors*. It is divided into two phases.

Phase 1 covers the basic medical sciences and lasts six terms. Teaching is in an interdisciplinary, systems-based format combining core material with a range of special study modules. A course in communication skills starts from day one and includes attachment to a local general practice. There are also courses in learning and study skills, first aid and information technology.

Phase 2 marks the start of the main clinical phase of the course and begins towards the end of Year 2. Clinical teaching takes place both in hospitals and the community and is supplemented by lectures, tutorials and seminars. Phase 2 also includes teaching in embryology, genetics, pathology, sociology and statistics. The final year allows students some flexibility in choosing attachments and includes a shadow house officer post.

ASSESSMENT

Students are assessed at the end of each clinical attachment by the team of which they have been a member. The main pathology course is undertaken and examined during Phase 2. There are examinations in clinical pharmacology and therapeutics, obstetrics & gynaecology, paediatrics and clinical genetics during the second clinical year. A final examination is held at the end of the final clinical year.

INTERCALATED DEGREE

Students are encouraged to undertake an intercalated Honours BSc degree, normally (but not always) at the end of Year 2. Nearly half of students do so, and financial support is given to over 80% of these. A variety of subject areas are available to intercalated BSc students. There is also an opportunity for a number of students to undertake a PhD within a shortened clinical phase.

ELECTIVE PERIOD

An elective period is available during the final clinical year. UMDS has links with the University of Lille and with Charles University in Prague.

AT A GLANCE

Applications received	**2993**
Offers made	**472**
Total accepted	**203**
Overseas accepted	**16**
Interview	**Yes**
Typical A level offer	**ABB**
Premedical course	**No**
Length of course	**5 years**
Degrees	**MB BS**
Intercalated degree	**BSc (optional)**
Elective period	**8–10 weeks**

LIVING NEAR UMDS

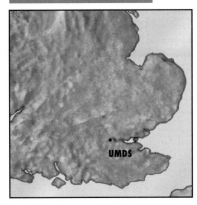

UMDS

ENTRY REQUIREMENTS

- 3 A levels **or** 2 A + 2 AS levels

- **must** include A or AS level Chemistry, plus one other A level (or two AS level) science or mathematical subject(s)

- GCSE grade C or above in English Language, Mathematics and Biology, unless offered at A or AS level

- double certification in a recognised Combined Science GCSE syllabus is acceptable

- passes in arts subjects are particularly welcomed, although General Studies is not acceptable

FURTHER INFORMATION

Applications from mature students are welcomed, although the medical school is less likely to accept those over the age of 30 years. UMDS is happy to agree to deferred entry as long as the year out will be used 'to good purpose'.

For information about open days, contact the Admissions Office. Videos about UMDS and living in London are available free of charge to schools and colleges from: Visible Productions Ltd, 3 The Flag Store, Jubilee Yard, Queen Elizabeth Street, London SE1 2LP.

UMDS is located just south of the Thames and within easy reach of such facilities as the Tate Gallery and the National Theatre. All undergraduates at UMDS become members of The United Clubs, which offer a wide variety of social, cultural and sporting activities ranging from rugby to wine appreciation. Weekly discos are organised and there are three Balls a year.

The medical school has two sports grounds (in South London and near Cobham in Surrey) with a range of facilities. In addition, there is a swimming pool at Guy's Hospital. Students also have the right to use the facilities of the University of London Union.

UNITED MEDICAL AND DENTAL SCHOOLS OF GUY'S AND ST THOMAS'S HOSPITALS

UNIVERSITY COLLEGE LONDON MEDICAL SCHOOL

Tutor to Medical Students
Faculty of Life Sciences
University College London
Gower Street
London WC1E 6BT

UCAS code: UCL U80 A100 MBBS

☎   (0171) 387 7050
Fax: (0171) 380 7920
WWW: http://www.ucl.ac.uk

The School of Medicine at UCL was inaugurated in 1987, combining five institutions which included the School of Medicine of University College London and the Middlesex Hospital Medical School. A link with the Royal Free Hospital School of Medicine is likely to occur in 1998 or 1999.

COURSE OUTLINE

A new curriculum is planned for 1998 or 1999, at the time of the planned link with the Royal Free.

Currently, **Year 1** of the basic medical sciences course concentrates on the fundamental aspects of human biology, with three major courses which include teaching via lectures, tutorials, practicals, clinical demonstrations and computer-assisted learning. Year 1 includes an optional course which can be in a subject unrelated to medicine, such as modern languages, and courses on medical statistics and biometry.

Year 2 considers how the body's normal structure and function is affected by disease. Students can choose a topic for in-depth supervised study, leading to a short dissertation. During the clinical course, teaching becomes more self-directed. In **Year 3** there are attachments in medicine, surgery, pathology and clinical pharmacology. Some teaching is also based in general practice. **Year 4** covers the major specialties in five eight-week blocks. Some of the time is spent at district general hospitals outside London. **Year 5** includes a longer district general hospital attachment, a choice of clinical attachments and an elective period.

ASSESSMENT

Continuous assessment during the basic medical sciences course contributes towards the course mark, although a major element comes from end-of-year examinations. Assessments during the clinical course do not generally contribute to the final examinations, held in September/October and June of the final clinical year.

INTERCALATED DEGREE

UCL offers a range of degree programmes for students (around 60%) who opt for a one-year intercalated Honours BSc degree. A combined eight-year MB PhD programme is also available for three or four students a year.

ELECTIVE PERIOD

A block in the final year is devoted to a period of elective study, which many students spend in the developing world.

AT A GLANCE

Applications received	**3380**
Offers made	**473**
Total accepted	**223**
Overseas accepted	**12**
Interview	**Yes**
Typical A level offer	**ABB**
Premedical course	**No**
Length of course	**5 years**
Degrees	**MB BS**
Intercalated degree	**BSc (optional)**
Elective period	**8 weeks**

LIVING NEAR UCL

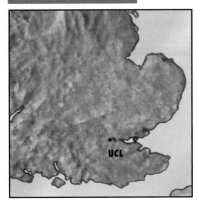

ENTRY REQUIREMENTS

- 3 A levels **or** 2 A + 2 AS levels

- **must** include A level or AS level Chemistry

- A level Physical Science can replace Chemistry, but not in combination with Physics

- two non-science A levels can be offered if the applicant has GCSE grade B (or above) passes in two separate sciences

- AS level Chemistry must be offered with at least one A level science or mathematics subject

- Mathematics and English at not less than GCSE grade B or equivalent

University College London is based in the relatively quiet district of Bloomsbury to the north of the Thames and yet is within easy reach of central London. Students become members of the University College London Union, but are also catered for by their own UCL Medical School Students' Union, which runs two bars and administers 26 clubs and societies covering a diversity of interests. The Union has access to the Middlesex Hospital's 20-acre sports ground at Chislehurst and the 60-acre UCL Sports Ground at Shenley in Hertfordshire. Students are also able to use the facilities provided by the University of London Union.

FURTHER INFORMATION

Applications are welcomed from mature applicants, but are only exceptionally considered over the age of 30 years, and never over 40 years. Applicants for graduate entry are expected to obtain at least an upper second class Honours degree.

Around 700 applicants are interviewed each year. Interviews are held on weekday mornings and include an opportunity to talk informally with students and staff.

UNIVERSITY COLLEGE LONDON MEDICAL SCHOOL

UNIVERSITY OF MANCHESTER MEDICAL SCHOOL

Admissions Officer
Faculty of Medicine
Stopford Building
The University of Manchester
Oxford Road
Manchester M13 9PT

UCAS codes: MANU M20 A104 MBChB/MedE (6 years)
MANU M20 A106 MBChB/Med (5 years)
MANU M20 A107 MBChB/Eur (5 years/Europe)

☎ (0161) 275 5025 – Admissions enquiries
Fax: (0161) 275 5584
WWW: http://www.man.ac.uk

Medicine has been taught in Manchester since the 1700s. The medical school introduced a revised curriculum in 1994.

COURSE OUTLINE

A one-year premedical course (A104) is available for students with good A levels, but who do not have the science qualifications for entry to Year 1. Eleven students were accepted on to A104 from 511 applicants in 1994–5.

Years 1 and 2 of the medical course (A106 & A107) are centred around the biomedical sciences, although the teaching is clinically related. There are four 12-week semesters during the two years, each with its own theme (diet and metabolism; cardiorespiratory fitness, abilities and disabilities; and life cycle). A wide range of different teaching methods are utilised during this phase of the course. In **Years 3 to 5** students meet patients and spend a large part of their time in teaching hospitals and general practice. The whole course is integrated with multidisciplinary teaching in small groups. Year 4 contains an options programme where students can spend 12 weeks studying a chosen option. Much of the training in Year 5 takes place in district general hospitals with 'shadowing' of house officers.

The European Programme: About ten students each year with a working knowledge of French and/or German can undertake part of their studies in France, Germany or Switzerland during Years 4 or 5. Students are eligible for this course if they have A level French or German, or AS level French and/or German. 'Out of hours' language tutorials are available during the first three years to help maintain language skills. Applicants for course A107 are also automatically considered for course A106.

INTERCALATED DEGREE

At the end of Year 2 or 3, students have an opportunity to take a one-year intercalated BSc in one of the medically-related sciences.

ELECTIVE PERIOD

An eight-week elective period takes place in Year 5. Students can study in Manchester, but most go elsewhere.

AT A GLANCE

Applications received	**2283 (A106)**
Offers made	**660 (A106)**
Total accepted	**230 (A106)**
Overseas accepted	**17 (A106)**
Interview	**Yes**
Typical A level offer	**ABB**
Premedical course	**Yes**
Length of course	**5 years***
Degrees	**MB ChB**
Intercalated degree	**BSc (optional)**
Elective period	**8 weeks**

(*6 years if premedical course taken)

ENTRY REQUIREMENTS

- 3 A levels **or** 2 A + 2 AS levels

- **must** include A level Chemistry or Physical Science

- various combinations are accepted – consult the prospectus for guidance

- GCSE or O level Mathematics, Physics and Biology (or Human Biology or Zoology) at grade B minimum (unless offered at A or AS level)

- ideally 8 passes at GCSE level, with six at grade A

FURTHER INFORMATION

A one-year premedical course (A104) is available for those who do not meet the requirements for direct entry to the medical course. Usually 10–20 places are available.

Candidates applying for deferred entry are considered. There are no stipulations on how the year out is spent.

Open days are usually held in the Spring and early Summer: contact the Admissions Officer in February/March for dates.

LIVING IN MANCHESTER

MANCHESTER

Manchester has undergone a significant revival in recent years. Due to host the Commonwealth Games in 2002, the city is justly proud of its sporting facilities, and in particular its football and cricket teams. The city has numerous cultural attractions (including the Hallé Orchestra and BBC Philharmonic) and the shopping facilities and nightlife are among the best outside of London. For outdoor enthusiasts, Cumbria and North Wales are relatively close at hand and the city has excellent travel connections, including a major international airport.

UNIVERSITY OF MANCHESTER MEDICAL SCHOOL

'Manchester has a new innovative course which is training more skilful, competent and confident doctors.'

'Manchester is a great place to be a student — whatever you want, we've got it!'

UNIVERSITY OF NEWCASTLE MEDICAL SCHOOL

The Medical School
University of Newcastle
Framlington Place
Newcastle upon Tyne NE2 4HH

UCAS code: NEWC N21 A104 MBBS/Med1 (premedical)
              NEWC N21 A106 MBBS/Med2 (stage 1 entry)

☎   (0191) 222 6000 ext. 7034 – Course enquiries
Fax: (0191) 222 6139
E-mail: admissions-enquiries@ncl.ac.uk
WWW: http://www.ncl.ac.uk

The teaching of medicine in Newcastle commenced in 1834. The current medical school building opened in 1984 and shares a site with the Royal Victoria Infirmary.

COURSE OUTLINE

Candidates without the necessary science A levels can apply for entry to the premedical year (A104); ten students were accepted on to A104 from 455 applicants in 1994–5. Most candidates enter the Stage 1 course directly (A106) and complete their training in five years.

In line with the *Tomorrow's Doctors* recommendations, the Newcastle medical curriculum consists of integrated interdisciplinary courses covering body systems rather than individual disciplines, with a clinical emphasis.

The first four semesters of the course are devoted to **Phase 1** (Stages 1 and 2), covering the basic sciences and systems of the body with an emphasis on clinical work and patient contact. **Phase 2** (Stages 3 and 4) begins with a 12-week clinical skills course, followed by a series of clinical attachments. Stage 3 lasts a total of 60 weeks and Stage 4 lasts 68 weeks. The first 21 weeks of Stage 4 comprise a series of special study modules. Following a summer elective period, students undertake attachments in Newcastle and throughout the northern region.

Prior to commencing the first house officer post, there is an intensive two-week training course.

ASSESSMENT

Examinations are held at the end of each semester, but emphasis is also placed upon continuous assessment. This includes projects, written work and in-course tests. Clinical skills are examined at the end of each clinical attachment.

INTERCALATED DEGREE

Selected students can undertake an additional year of study in one or more of the basic sciences, including supervised research, leading to an Honours Bachelor of Medical Science degree. About 10–15% choose to do so. Exceptional students may then seek entry to a combined MB-PhD programme lasting seven years and one term.

ELECTIVE PERIOD

A nine-week elective period in the summer of Stage 4 can be undertaken in the UK or overseas.

AT A GLANCE

Applications received	**1836 (A106)**
Offers made	**265 (A106)**
Total accepted	**143 (A106)**
Overseas accepted	**10 (A106)**
Interview	**Yes**
Typical A level offer	**ABB**
Premedical course	**Yes**
Length of course	**5 years***
Degrees	**MB BS**
Intercalated degree	**BMedSci (optional)**
Elective period	**9 weeks**

(*6 years if premedical course taken)

ENTRY REQUIREMENTS

- 3 A levels **or** 2 A + 2 AS levels

- **must** include Chemistry at A or AS level

- General Studies **not** acceptable

- GCSE (or equivalent) Mathematics, Physics and a biological subject, or Mathematics and a double pass in Combined or Integrated Science GCSE, unless offered at A or AS level

FURTHER INFORMATION

Deferred entry is allowed as long as students have constructive plans for the year out.

Four visit days are held each year. For information and bookings (at least two weeks in advance) contact: Schools Liaison Office, ☎ (0191) 222 8675. A videotape (*One Newcastle University*) is available for schools and colleges from the Schools Liaison Office, ☎ (0191) 222 8669/6094.

LIVING IN NEWCASTLE

The city of Newcastle has over quarter of a million residents and boasts excellent shopping and leisure facilities.

Newcastle Medical School has an active students' society which organises regular sports and social events. The medical school has its own gymnasium and there is a medics' sports club on the city's outskirts.

UNIVERSITY OF NEWCASTLE MEDICAL SCHOOL

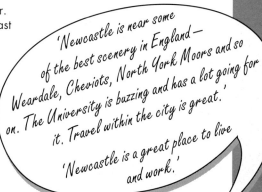

'Newcastle is near some of the best scenery in England – Weardale, Cheviots, North York Moors and so on. The University is buzzing and has a lot going for it. Travel within the city is great.'

'Newcastle is a great place to live and work.'

UNIVERSITY OF NOTTINGHAM MEDICAL SCHOOL

UNIVERSITY OF NOTTINGHAM MEDICAL SCHOOL
Admissions Officer
Medical School Faculty Office
Queen's Medical Centre
Nottingham NG7 2UH

UCAS code: NOTTM N84 A100 BMBS/Med

☎   (0115) 970 9379
Fax: (0115) 970 9384
WWW: http://www.nott.ac.uk

The University of Nottingham Medical School opened in 1970 with an intake of 48 medical students. It rapidly expanded to become one of the largest medical schools in the country, with an annual intake of 170 students. A new curriculum had been fully implemented by 1996.

COURSE OUTLINE
The emphasis of the five-year medical course is on the integration of basic sciences and clinical medicine, with exposure to patients from the first year onward.

Years 1 to 3 of the medical course are divided into six semesters. Semesters 1 to 4 are devoted to basic medical sciences, taught as four main 'themes': molecular and cellular aspects of medicine; human structure and function; health care in the community; and personal and professional development. Students undertake a research project during Semester 5 which, together with other forms of assessment, contributes toward the BMedSci (Hons) degree that is normally awarded at the end of Year 3. Semester 6 is devoted to an Introduction to Medicine and Surgery course, leading into the main Clinical Practice course that occupies **Years 4 and 5**.

ASSESSMENT
Assessment for the BMedSci degree is divided into two parts. Part I is based upon a number of examinations that are held during Years 1 and 2 of the medical course. Part II is based upon a dissertation, written papers and *viva voce* examination. The BMedSci degree is awarded at the end of Year 3. In the event of the Faculty Board refusing entry to the clinical course, a student would have to carry out further approved work during Semester 6 to qualify for the BMedSci degree, rather than going on to the Introduction to Medicine and Surgery course.

During the main Clinical Practice course, students are examined by means of assessments at the end of major attachments. Examinations include assessment by objective structured clinical examination and multiple-choice questionnaires. Students also carry log books which are used to monitor their progress in learning clinical skills.

INTERCALATED DEGREE
In Nottingham the BMedSci degree is an integrated part of the medical course (see above).

ELECTIVE PERIOD
Students undertake a ten-week elective period and are encouraged to work away from Nottingham.

AT A GLANCE

Applications received	**2867**
Offers made	**348**
Total accepted	**183**
Overseas accepted	**25**
Interview	**Yes**
Typical A level offer	**ABB**
Premedical course	**No**
Length of course	**5 years**
Degrees	**BMedSci BM BS**
Intercalated degree	**BMedSci (compulsory)**
Elective period	**10 weeks**

ENTRY REQUIREMENTS

- 3 A levels **or** 2 A + 2 AS levels

- **must** include A level Chemistry, one other science and a third mainstream academic subject

- GCSE Mathematics, Physics, Biology (**not** Human Biology) and English, unless offered at A level

- 6 grade As at GCSE level (preferably including the sciences)

FURTHER INFORMATION

Student visits can be made at the time of the interview, which includes an opportunity to meet current students. It is not possible to arrange visits at other times.

Students wishing to defer entry will be expected to undertake 'constructive' work during their time out, such as work or travel in a medically-related field.

LIVING IN NOTTINGHAM

NOTTINGHAM

The University of Nottingham campus is three miles from the city centre and is based around land provided by Sir Jesse Boot, founder of Boots Pharmaceuticals. The campus boasts a large sports centre and swimming pool. Nottingham is well-known for its football teams and its cricket team (based at Trent Bridge), and is also home to the National Water Sports Centre.

Nottingham offers a varied social and cultural life, including the famous Goose Fair, held every October. By virtue of its central location, living in Nottingham also puts you within easy reach of many other major towns and cities, and for outdoor pursuits the Peak District is just a short distance away.

'The emphasis is very much on student-centred learning, which requires good time management and motivation.' 'Nottingham is a very "progressive" medical school and is proud of its position as one of the most popular medical schools.'

UNIVERSITY OF NOTTINGHAM MEDICAL SCHOOL

UNIVERSITY OF OXFORD MEDICAL SCHOOL

Medical School Offices
John Radcliffe Hospital
Headington
Oxford OX3 9DU

UCAS code: OXF 033 A100 BMBCh

Enquiries to the Medical School Offices by letter are preferred to telephone calls
☎   (01865) 270207 – Oxford Colleges Admissions Service
       (01865) 270211 – Oxford Colleges Admissions Service
WWW: http://www.ox.ac.uk

The medical curriculum at Oxford has a strong scientific emphasis and there is a clear-cut division between the preclinical and clinical courses. All medical students are required to study for an Honours degree (see below).

COURSE OUTLINE

The preclinical course lasts nine terms (three years). There is little patient contact during the preclinical years, although clinically-related points are used to illustrate the coursework.

Terms 1 to 3 cover the material needed for Part I of the First BM examination: morphology, reproduction and development; physiology and pharmacology; and biochemistry. There is also a course in elementary statistics. **Terms 4 and 5** cover integrated courses in systems of the body; neural, behavioural and neuroendocrine systems; and pathology and medical genetics, leading to Part II of the First BM examination. **Terms 6 to 9** are spent in study at a more advanced level for the Honours School of Physiological Sciences. Students take a general paper in physiological sciences and may present a dissertation instead of one written paper.

The **clinical course** may be undertaken at Oxford or elsewhere. Students wishing to go to other medical schools for their clinical training must take a course and qualifying examination in medical sociology. Students taking the three-year Oxford course must apply competitively during Year 3. Around half stay in Oxford; the remainder go to London, Cambridge or elsewhere.

ASSESSMENT

Intermittent assessments monitor progress in some practicals. Otherwise, all courses are assessed by conventional three-hour examinations, which include essay and short-note questions.

INTERCALATED DEGREE

All students study for an Honours degree. This is almost always Physiological Sciences, although Psychology, Philosophy and Physiology (PPP) is possible with a further year's study.

ELECTIVE PERIOD

The nature and duration of the elective period will depend upon where the clinical course is undertaken (ten weeks on the Oxford course).

AT A GLANCE

Applications received	**732**
Offers made	**99**
Total accepted	**97**
Overseas accepted	**8**
Interview	**Yes**
Typical A level offer	**AAA**
Premedical course	**No**
Length of course	**6 years**
Degrees	**BM BCh**
Intercalated degree	**BA (compulsory)**
Elective period	**See previous page**

ENTRY REQUIREMENTS

- 3 A levels **or** 2 A + 2 AS levels

- two Science/Mathematics A levels plus one A level (or two AS levels) in any subject, **or**

- two Science/Mathematics AS levels plus one Science/Mathematics A level, plus one A level in any subject

- **must** include A or AS level Chemistry

- GCSE passes (grade C or above) in Biology, Mathematics, Physics and English, if not offered at A or AS level

- double award Science may be substituted for GCSE Biology and Physics

- various equivalent examinations are acceptable – see the prospectus for more information

FURTHER INFORMATION

Application to Oxford (and Cambridge) starts earlier than for other universities – consult the current prospectus for more details. Shortlisted candidates are required to undertake a short, written test at the time of their interview.

Many colleges organise visit days and there are two departmental open days each year, usually in June. Further information can be obtained from the Oxford Colleges Admissions Service (OCAS)– see previous page. Oxford University Student Union publishes an *Alternative Prospectus* and the *Oxford Handbook* (both priced), obtainable from: Student Union Offices, New Barnett House, 28 Little Clarendon Street, Oxford OX1 2HU, ☎ (01865) 270777.

LIVING IN OXFORD

OXFORD

One of Oxford's strengths lies in its collegiate system. Each student's social life tends to revolve around their college, particularly during the preclinical years. A huge range of social activities is available at both a college and university level. Although the city itself is not renowned for its nightlife, there are nonetheless numerous pubs and restaurants to choose from.

'The medical course at Oxford remains more traditional than most, with a clear separation between preclinical and clinical years. You therefore need to think very carefully whether the course's strength – its emphasis on the science of medicine – appeals more to you than early contact with patients.'

UNIVERSITY OF OXFORD MEDICAL SCHOOL

67

UNIVERSITY OF SHEFFIELD MEDICAL SCHOOL *(sidebar)*

UNIVERSITY OF SHEFFIELD MEDICAL SCHOOL

Sub-Dean for Admissions
Medical School
University of Sheffield
Beech Hill Road
Sheffield S10 2RX

UCAS code: SHEFD S18 A104 MBChB/Med1 (1st year entry)
SHEFD S18 A106 MBChB/Med2 (2nd year entry)

☎ (0114) 271 2142
WWW: http://www.shef.ac.uk

The medical school at Sheffield dates from the early 1800s, predating the University. It is located in the same building as the Royal Hallamshire Hospital.

COURSE OUTLINE

A new medical course was introduced in 1994, in line with the *Tomorrow's Doctors* report, adopting a systems-based approach to teaching with an emphasis on patient contact and small-group teaching. The course is divided into four stages.

Stage 0 occupies Year 1 and forms the premedical course (A104) for applicants who do not have the necessary A or AS levels for direct entry to Year 2. Seventeen students were accepted on to A104 from 921 applicants in 1994–5.

Stage 1 covers Years 2 and 3 and comprises teaching in the basic medical sciences. This stage consists of nine modules. Eight of these are systems-based and sequential, and one (*Health and Society*) integrates with them. A Family Attachment scheme, to which 20 hours is devoted, places students in contact with a GP and with a family about to experience a birth.

Stage 2, in Year 4, is devoted to the development of foundation clinical skills and is mostly taught on the wards. **Stage 3** is the final stage, in Years 5 and 6, encompassing the refinement of clinical skills, special study modules and an overseas elective period.

ASSESSMENT

Assessment of each module in Stage 1 is by 50% multiple-choice examination and 50% project work (essays, posters, presentations and practicals). During Stage 2, students keep a logbook to record the development of their clinical skills. This contributes to the overall assessment of the year, together with a multiple-choice examination, written case histories and a clinical examination. Stage 3 assessment includes project work, multiple-choice and written examinations, objective structured clinical examinations and traditional clinical examinations.

ELECTIVE PERIOD

A ten-week overseas elective period is taken during Stage 3.

AT A GLANCE

Applications received	**2237 (A106)**
Offers made	**458 (A106)**
Total accepted	**169 (A106)**
Overseas accepted	**10 (A106)**
Interview	**Yes**
Typical A level offer	**ABB**
Premedical course	**Yes**
Length of course	**5 years***
Degrees	**MB ChB**
Intercalated degree	**No**
Elective period	**10 weeks**

(*6 years if premedical course taken)

ENTRY REQUIREMENTS

- 3 A levels **or** 2 A + 2 AS levels

- A level Chemistry plus one A level in one of Biology, Physics or Mathematics, plus one A or two AS levels in any subjects, **or**

- AS level Chemistry plus two from Biology, Mathematics and Physics (one A and one AS level), plus one further A level in any subject

- Physical Science may replace A level Chemistry or Physics (but not both)

- Biology at A level may be replaced by Botany, Human Biology, Social Biology or Zoology

- excellent GCSE passes, including sciences (may be a dual award), Mathematics and English

FURTHER INFORMATION

Visit days are arranged by the Schools and Colleges Liaison Service and must be booked in advance. The Service also has videos on the University (*The Undergrads' Universal Guide to Sheffield*) and the medical course. In addition, an alternative prospectus is available free of charge.

For further details, contact: Schools and Colleges Liaison Service, The

University of Sheffield, 14 Favell Road, Sheffield S3 7QX, ☎ (0114) 282 4226.

LIVING IN SHEFFIELD

SHEFFIELD

Sheffield is Yorkshire's second city (after Leeds) and is the fifth largest in the UK. Partly as a result of hosting the World Student Games in 1991, Sheffield has a number of excellent sports venues. The city is home to the Sheffield Wednesday and Sheffield United football clubs, and to the national diving and volleyball squads.

The University has several sports facilities of its own, and is particularly proud of its 33-metre indoor swimming pool. For those with more cultural interests, the city offers some good art galleries (including the award-winning Ruskin Gallery) and museums. Further afield, those who enjoy outdoor pursuits will find the Peak District National Park within easy reach.

UNIVERSITY OF SHEFFIELD MEDICAL SCHOOL

UNIVERSITY OF SOUTHAMPTON MEDICAL SCHOOL

Admissions Tutor
Admissions Office
University of Southampton
Biomedical Sciences Building
Bassett Crescent East
Southampton SO16 7PX

UCAS code: SOTON S27 A100 BM/Med

☎   (01703) 594408
Fax: (01703) 594159
WWW: http://www.soton.ac.uk

The University of Southampton Medical School forms a part of the new Faculty of Medicine, Health and Biological Sciences that was established in 1995. The medical school has taken the *Tomorrow's Doctors* report into account in planning its curriculum and places a strong emphasis on integrated teaching.

COURSE OUTLINE

Most basic science teaching occurs during **Years 1 and 2**, although some continues into Year 3. Following an initial Foundation Term, a series of systems courses integrate teaching around the systems of the body. Teaching is by means of lectures, laboratory practicals, group teaching, projects and discussion sessions. The clinical relevance of the basic sciences is emphasised and some clinical demonstrations involving patients are arranged.

Year 3 starts with the development of clinical skills, followed by their consolidation with a variety of clinical attachments in medicine, surgery, obstetrics & gynaecology, child health, psychiatry, geriatric medicine and palliative care. There are also regular sessions in general practice. **Year 4** begins with an eight-week elective period, followed by an eight-month period of 'study in depth' where students can concentrate on a project of interest. This occurs in conjunction with further clinical attachments. During **Year 5** there are several clinical attachments based around regional hospitals and general practice.

ASSESSMENT

In-course assessments are used to provide feedback for students and teaching staff, in addition to forming part of the assessment for the Primary, Intermediate and Final BM examinations. Assessment of the eight-month 'study in depth' period during Year 4 is based upon a project report.

INTERCALATED DEGREE

Medical students may be accepted to work towards an intercalated degree depending upon their results in the Intermediate examination. Two degrees are available: an Intercalated BSc (Hons) or BSc (Social Sciences) (Hons).

ELECTIVE PERIOD

There is an eight-week elective period at the start of Year 4. Many students choose to undertake clinical work abroad and there are limited funds to help students with travel costs.

AT A GLANCE

Applications received	**2441**
Offers made	**488**
Total accepted	**156**
Overseas accepted	**11**
Interview	**Seldom**
Typical A level offer	**ABB**
Premedical course	**No**
Length of course	**5 years**
Degrees	**BM**
Intercalated degree	**BSc (optional)**
Elective period	**8 weeks**

ENTRY REQUIREMENTS

- 3 A levels **or** 2 A + 2 AS levels

- **must** include A level Chemistry or Physical Science, although Chemistry AS level is acceptable with at least one other AS level science subject

- GCSE Biology, English, Physics and Mathematics unless offered at A level

- Integrated/Combined science can be offered in lieu of separate Biology/Physics GCSEs

- six grade As at GCSE level (preferably including the sciences)

FURTHER INFORMATION

Southampton encourages applications from mature candidates, usually age 30 or below, and reserves about 25 places per year for them. All mature applicants are interviewed. Graduates are normally expected to offer at least an upper second class degree.

Deferred entry is encouraged for candidates wishing to work, travel or undertake voluntary service.

Visit days are arranged for prospective applicants: for further details contact the Admissions Tutor – see previous page. A university video is also available. For further details,

contact: Academic Registrars Department (Video), University of Southampton, Highfield, Southampton SO17 1BJ.

LIVING IN SOUTHAMPTON

The south-coast city of Southampton is best known for its maritime role, which continues today. Not surprisingly, it offers a wide range of watersports, but it is also home to a Premier League football club and Hampshire County Cricket Club.

The University has around 9000 full-time undergraduate students based around an attractive campus which has its own art gallery, concert hall and theatre. The Students' Union is home to a range of facilities including a travel centre, launderette and video shop. The Union offers over 200 clubs and societies catering for a variety of interests, and also organises regular social events.

UNIVERSITY OF SOUTHAMPTON MEDICAL SCHOOL

UNIVERSITY OF ST ANDREWS MEDICAL SCHOOL

The Pro Dean (Medical Science)
Faculties Office
79 North Street
St Andrews
FIFE KY16 9AJ

UCAS code: STA S36 A108 BSc/McSc

☎   (01334) 463324 – Schools Liaison Service
     (01334) 476161 – University
Fax: (01334) 463330
WWW: http://www.st-andrews.ac.uk

Medical science is the only pre-clinical programme offered by St Andrews, leading to a general BSc (Medical Science) in three years or an Honours BSc (Medical Science) in four years. All graduates are guaranteed a clinical place at the University of Manchester for a further three years of clinical studies.

At the time of writing, the University was planning changes to its course in response to the *Tomorrow's Doctors* recommendations, including an increase in the amount of teaching in behavioural science, full utilisation of community resources and the introduction of special study modules.

COURSE OUTLINE

The emphasis of the medical science programme is on basic scientific principles, although throughout the curriculum the courses are related to a clinical context. During Year 2, students make hospital visits and attachments are organised with local GPs.

During **Year 1**, the courses undertaken are molecular chemistry, human anatomy and human physiology. Training is provided in first aid and students must obtain a certificate before graduating. **Year 2** comprises further teaching in human anatomy and human physiology together with a short course in statistics. **Year 3** courses include applied medical science, medical microbiology, pathology and pharmacology, plus short courses in psychology applied to medicine and public health medicine.

ASSESSMENT

To continue through the programme, students must attain the required number of passes each year.

INTERCALATED DEGREE

During Year 3 selection is made for the Honours programme. Selected students are those who display particular interest and aptitude in their studies. The intercalated fourth year allows students to undertake advanced study and supervised research work leading to a dissertation.

ELECTIVE PERIOD

See University of Manchester entry.

AT A GLANCE

Applications received	**834**
Offers made	**427**
Total accepted	**112**
Overseas accepted	**7**
Interview	**No**
Typical A level offer	**ABB**
Typical SCE Highers offer	**AAABB**
Premedical course	**No**
Length of course	**3 years***
Degrees	**BSc (Medical Science)**
Intercalated degree	**Optional**
Elective period	**See previous page**

(*4 years for the intercalated Honours degree)
(plus 3-year clinical course at Manchester)

ENTRY REQUIREMENTS

- 3 A levels, including Chemistry and either Mathematics or Physics, **or**

- 2 A + 2 AS levels, including Chemistry and either Mathematics or Physics, **or**

- 5 SCE Highers, including Chemistry and either Mathematics or Physics

- if either Mathematics or Physics is not taken as A or AS levels, or SCE Highers, there must be a GCSE or SCE Standard Grade pass in the subject

- English at GCSE or SCE Standard Grade pass

FURTHER INFORMATION

An alternative prospectus can be purchased from: Schools Liaison Service, University of St Andrews, Old Union Building, Butts Wynd, St Andrews, Fife KY16 9AJ.

A Faculty Open Day is held each summer for school parties – contact the Faculty Office for details. Individual visits can be arranged via the

Associate Director (address above). Two further open days are also held in December and January for those applicants offered a place.

LIVING IN ST ANDREWS

Located on the Fife coast, St Andrews is a small and attractive city that is perhaps best known for its golfing associations. The total population is around 16,000, around 6000 of whom are university students and staff. The city has a number of pubs, restaurants and cafés, as well as a two-screen cinema.

The University has a medical students' society (the Bute Medical Society) that organises regular meetings and social events. There is also a University Sports Centre (as well as a sports centre in the city itself). Those who enjoy outdoor pursuits will find the Grampian mountains near at hand.

UNIVERSITY OF WALES COLLEGE OF MEDICINE

Undergraduate Admissions Officer
University of Wales College of Medicine
Heath Park
Cardiff CF4 4XN

UCAS code: WCM W10 A104 MBBCh/MedF (1st MB BCh)
                WCM W10 A106 MBBCh/Med (2nd MB BCh)

☎   (01222) 742027 – Undergraduate Admissions Officer
Fax: (01222) 742914
WWW: http://www.uwcm.ac.uk

The University of Wales College of Medicine was established as a medical school in 1931 and changed its name from the Welsh National School of Medicine in 1984. It is one of the six colleges comprising the University of Wales, the second largest university in the UK.

COURSE OUTLINE

The complete medical course lasts six years, although nearly all candidates enter directly into the Second MB BCh course at Year 2.

Year 1 comprises a First MB BCh Medical Science Foundation Course (A104) for applicants who cannot meet the requirements for direct entry into Year 2. Thirteen students were accepted on to A104 from 409 applicants in 1994–5.

The course structure was recently reviewed and the preclinical/clinical divide was removed, allowing students contact with patients from the beginning. The curriculum consists of a core course accompanied by special study modules. **Years 2 and 3** concentrate on the body systems in health and disease. There are short clinical attachments in local hospitals and with GPs. **Year 4** focuses on the development of clinical skills and includes an extended case study of a chronic illness together with two extended special study modules. **Years 5 and 6** include further clinical attachments in hospitals and with GPs and a period of preparation for the house officer post.

ASSESSMENT

There are regular in-course assessments which provide feedback and contribute to the overall marks. There are also formal examinations and assessments of the project work undertaken for special study modules. The main examinations take place in Year 2 (Primary MB), Year 4 (Intermediate MB) and Year 6 (Final MB).

INTERCALATED DEGREE

Around 15–20% of students study for an intercalated degree, undertaken in the basic medical sciences at the end of Year 3 or in more clinically-oriented subjects at the end of Year 5.

ELECTIVE PERIOD

During the final year an eight-week elective period may be undertaken in the UK or abroad. The mark given for a written report forms part of the final degree examination. Some elective period scholarships are available and there is an Elective Studies Adviser.

AT A GLANCE

Applications received	**1305 (A106)**
Offers made	**479 (A106)**
Total accepted	**153 (A106)**
Overseas accepted	**17 (A106)**
Interview	**Yes**
Typical A level offer	**ABB**
Premedical course	**Yes**
Length of course	**5 years***
Degrees	**MB BCh**
Intercalated degree	**Optional**
Elective period	**8 weeks**

(*6 years if premedical course taken)

ENTRY REQUIREMENTS

- A level Chemistry plus two from Biology (or Zoology), Physics and Mathematics, **or**

- A level Chemistry plus two approved subjects (one normally Physics or Biology)

- GCSE, O level or AS level Biology and Physics if not passed at A level

- the A grade at A level must be attained in Chemistry, Biology or Physics

- 2 AS levels acceptable instead of one non-specified A level

FURTHER INFORMATION

Approximately 12 places per year are available on a First MB BCh course (UCAS code A104) for those who do not meet the requirements for direct entry to Year 2.

Students offering a European language as their third A level subject are encouraged to apply. Opportunities for European exchanges are available within the curriculum.

Visits are arranged to the Medical College virtually every month. A videotape is also available for free loan. For further information contact the Undergraduate Admissions Officer.

LIVING IN CARDIFF

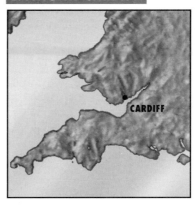

The city of Cardiff in South Wales offers a range of social and sporting facilities. It has an active nightlife, with numerous pubs and clubs, and there is a variety of music venues. The National Sports Centre for Wales is located in Cardiff, as is Cardiff Arms Park, the national stadium and central focus of Welsh rugby.

Medical students become members of the University of Wales Cardiff Students' Union, which organises a freshers' fortnight at the start of each academic year.

Outside Cardiff, students with an interest in outdoor pursuits can find the Brecon Beacons and the beaches of the Gower Coast. The city also has excellent links with the rest of the UK (London is less than two hours away by rail).

UNIVERSITY OF WALES COLLEGE OF MEDICINE

CHAPTER FOUR

Applying via UCAS

Medical school applications must be made through the Universities and Colleges Admissions Service (UCAS). You should be able to obtain a copy of the application form and *UCAS Handbook* from your school or college. If you have left school, or are resident abroad, you can obtain these items direct from UCAS. Don't forget to include the necessary payment (payable to 'UCAS') to cover postage and packing if you are writing from outside the UK. Forms and Handbooks are also available from British Council Offices.

Once you have obtained your *UCAS Handbook*, read it carefully so that you clearly understand how to complete your application form. Every year, 25% of forms are found to contain errors which need to be referred back to the applicants, slowing up the whole process. Make sure you get it right first time! Your school will also be willing to give you advice on how to complete your form. In addition, a book and video, entitled *How to Complete your UCAS Form*, can be purchased from Trotman & Co. Ltd (see Further Reading).

Before you start filling in the original copy of your UCAS form, make a number of photocopies to practise on. Only when you are happy with the finished result should you transfer all your details over to the real form. If you do make errors on the real form, however, don't hesitate to obtain another copy. Refer to the *UCAS Handbook*, the instructions that come with the form and the individual medical school prospectuses while you fill in the form.

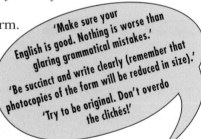

'Make sure your English is good. Nothing is worse than glaring grammatical mistakes.'

'Be succinct and write clearly (remember that photocopies of the form will be reduced in size).'

'Try to be original. Don't overdo the clichés!'

General points

When you submit your application form to UCAS, it will be photocopied and reduced to approximately two-thirds of its original size before being sent on to admissions tutors. It is therefore essential that you:

- write clearly,
- use black ballpoint or black type,

and that you:

- do not write outside the framework provided,
- do not attach extra sheets,
- do not stick sheets on to the form,
- do not detach the two halves of the form.

If you need to include additional information but cannot fit it on to the form, send it *direct* to the institutions *after* you have received the letter from UCAS acknowledging your application, quoting your name, address, application number and course code(s). You should note that the number at the top right-hand corner of the UCAS form is *not* your application number. Your application number will be notified to you *after* your form has been processed.

It should, of course, go without saying that everything you write on the form should be correct and complete. Indeed, you have to sign a declaration that this is the case at the end of the form. If an institution discovers that you have made a false statement, or have omitted significant information from your form, it has the right to withdraw or amend its offer, or to terminate your registration at the institution.

'Make sure you have done what you claim, otherwise you'll be rumbled at interview.'
'Don't lie – they will find out!'

Completing the UCAS form

Title, name and address

The form begins by asking you to fill in your title (Mr, Miss, Ms, etc.), followed by your surname/family name and then first/given name(s).

Your correspondence address, including your postcode (UK only), should be the one to which you want UCAS and the institutions to send all correspondence. Contact telephone and fax numbers should be those where you are most likely to be contacted over the next year.

If your correspondence address is different from your home address, your home address (and contact numbers) also needs to be entered. Finally, you should give your previous surname/family name, if applicable.

Further details

The further details requested include:

- your age on a given date,
- your sex,
- your date of birth,
- disabilities or special needs,
- registration number for vocational qualifications,
- who will pay your fees.

If you were born outside the UK, you are asked to insert the date you first entered the UK as a permanent resident.

You are also asked for your residential category (using the codes supplied by UCAS), area of permanent residence, country of birth and nationality.

Applications

In this section you are asked to list your applications in *UCAS Handbook* order – you do not have to indicate preferences at this stage. You should read the Handbook carefully, together with the individual institutions' prospectuses, before you complete this section.

Although you may choose up to six courses, one per line, the Council of Deans of UK Medical Schools and Faculties recommend that *no more than five choices* from the possible six should be used for either medical or dental courses. The remaining choice(s) can be used for an alternative course(s). The reason for this recommendation is that, if you don't gain an offer from these five choices, it is unlikely that you will be successful using a larger number.

When completing this section be careful to fill in the correct codes for each of your choices. You must check these in the current copy of the *UCAS Handbook*. An example of a code is as follows:

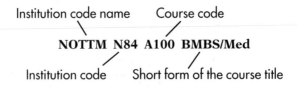

The code for Queen Mary and Westfield College also includes a campus code:

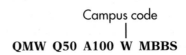

Write each entry on a separate line and do not leave any blank lines between entries. If you want to apply to more than one course at the same institution, you must place each choice on a separate line.

If further details are requested in the Handbook or prospectus, you must enter these in column (*f*). If the medical school has agreed that you can be considered for entry to a particular year, enter that year (e.g. **2**) in column (*g*). Enter an **H** in column (*h*) if you expect to live at home while attending the institution. If you wish to defer entry to a course for a year, tick the appropriate box(es) in column (*j*).

If you have previously applied through UCAS for any of your choices, you must enter the application number of your most recent application and the institution code(s) at the foot of this section.

Secondary education

In the secondary education section you must enter, in date order, the name and brief address of the three most recent secondary schools, colleges, and/or universities you have attended or are attending. You should enter the dates of attendance and whether your attendance was part-time, full-time or sandwich.

Record of Achievement

You should tick the appropriate box if you have a pre-16 or post-16 Record of Achievement (RoA). RoA documentation should *not* be sent to UCAS.

Planning statistics

The form also asks for information which is used for statistical and planning purposes but which does *not* form part of the selection process. You are asked to enter the occupational background of the parent (or step-parent or guardian) with the highest income in your household. You should enter your own occupation if you are over 21 years of age. UK applicants are also asked to enter a code describing their ethnic origin.

Qualifications

This section is usually divided into two, for *qualifications completed* and *qualifications pending*. Details of qualifications completed should include any examinations or assessments which you have failed. You are then asked to enter details of qualifications pending. Detailed instructions for the completion of these sections are supplied with the application form.

Special needs

If you have entered any disabilities or special needs earlier in the form, you should describe these more fully in the special needs section, together with details of any help you require.

Employment to date

If you have been in employment, you should enter details where requested. Weekend work, vacation work and work experience may all be included.

Personal statement

Your *personal statement* is without doubt one of the most important parts of the form. This section gives you an opportunity to win over the admissions tutors and explain your motivation. Most of all, this is your chance to make your form *stand out from the rest*. A look at the statistics in chapter 3 will reveal just how many applications (and, therefore, UCAS forms) are received by each medical school – at least hundreds, often thousands. Most applicants will have good qualifications and look fairly similar on the first two pages of the form. The personal statement is your opportunity to let your individual characteristics shine through and, hopefully, put other applicants in the shade.

Although you are not obliged to fill the section completely, it is a good idea to make the best possible use of the space available. Bear in mind, though, that you are *not* allowed to attach additional pages. The overall appearance of the section should be as good as the content, so avoid any errors or corrections and make sure it is easily legible (don't forget the medical schools receive a copy of the form that has been reduced to two-thirds the original size).

You will find some useful suggestions on structuring the section in the instructions supplied with the form. It is essential that you practise filling out photocopies of the form until you are happy with what you have written – only then should you complete the original.

Your aims in the personal statement are to:

- explain why you want to be a doctor;
- demonstrate your commitment to a career in medicine;
- describe your participation in school and the community;
- highlight your achievements;
- describe your hobbies and interests;
- explain any plans you may have for a year out.

WHY YOU WANT TO BE A DOCTOR

This question is almost certain to be asked at your interview and is discussed in detail in chapter 5. Indeed, you should read through that chapter before you write anything on your UCAS form. The space you have for your personal statement is limited, so don't go into great detail about your motivation. The important thing is to stress your interest in medicine and to provide supporting evidence that demonstrates your commitment.

YOUR COMMITMENT TO A CAREER IN MEDICINE

It is one thing to claim that you have an interest in medicine, and another to have taken active steps to demonstrate this interest. Long before you reach the stage of completing your UCAS form, you should have arranged voluntary work in local hospitals, nursing homes or hospices. A candidate who has spent time helping others is far more impressive than someone who has not taken the initiative to gain experience of working in a medical environment. Again, this is discussed in more detail in the following chapter.

Write a paragraph on where you have worked and for how long, and describe what the work involved. For example:

> 'Last summer I worked at the Hillview Nursing Home for two days each week, assisting residents with everyday tasks such as washing, dressing and eating meals. In doing so I increased my awareness and understanding of the challenges faced by the elderly and those who care for them.'

Don't copy the above example (or any other) word-for-word, but use it as a model to help structure your own paragraph.

YOUR PARTICIPATION IN SCHOOL AND THE COMMUNITY

Good interpersonal skills are essential for a prospective doctor, not only for working with patients but also for interacting with colleagues. Being a doctor also requires a commitment not only to the hospital community but also the wider community in which you work. In addition, good social skills are important for living and working within the 'community' of a medical school.

'Do different, unusual things in 5th/6th form to make sure you stand out from the others. We've all done "visiting the elderly", but we've not all done the Great North Run or taken handicapped children on holiday.'

'Don't overemphasise work experience which is not medical. I did eight weeks at an engineering firm and was asked why I didn't want to do engineering at every interview.'

Medical school selectors will therefore hope to see that you have already demonstrated your willingness to contribute to the life of your school and to your local community. Mention your membership of school clubs and societies and what you have contributed to them. Also mention any events, such as school plays or fund-raising events, that you have participated in. You should emphasise your organisational and interpersonal skills.

By undertaking voluntary work (see above) you will have shown some commitment to your community. Make sure you also mention any other activities you have participated in at a local level, for example supporting the activities of local charities, helping at a local youth club or participating in a scout group:

> 'At school I am a member of the drama group and recently played the role of Oberon in our production of *A Midsummer Night's Dream*. On Saturday afternoons I work as a voluntary assistant at a charity shop that is run to support a local hospice, and earlier this year I helped to organise a jumble sale to raise funds for new medical equipment.'

YOUR ACHIEVEMENTS

The aim of listing your achievements is to illustrate your commitment, motivation and determination to succeed. Obvious examples are any awards and distinctions you have received, including academic, music and sporting prizes and Duke of Edinburgh's Awards. However, don't overlook any unique or unusual achievements even if they didn't qualify for 'formal' recognition, such as climbing Ben Nevis or managing to complete a marathon.

YOUR HOBBIES AND INTERESTS

Medical school selectors are interested in your hobbies, as they like to take on well-rounded students who will be interesting to work with and contribute to the life of the medical school. Don't just make a list of what you do in your spare time, but try to expand upon your interests a little to add some colour. As before, try and concentrate on hobbies where you have made an active contribution and where you have worked with others, for example:

'Don't put down interests such as reading, gardening and so on unless you have a genuine interest, otherwise this comes across as a person who can't think of anything else to write.'

> 'I enjoy hockey and play in goal for the school team. I regularly attend local matches and write match reports for the school newspaper. I also enjoy dressmaking, and I help design and create costumes for the school drama group.'

PLANS FOR A YEAR OUT

If you intend to defer entry to medical school for a year, you should take a paragraph to explain what you are planning to do during that time. Some medical schools take a keener interest than others in your intentions for a year out, but it is always a good idea to demonstrate that you have considered it carefully and have detailed and realistic plans for how you intend to use your time.

MATURE STUDENTS

Mature students should apply the same principles as school students to the completion of the personal statement – namely, emphasising their interest in medicine and suitability as a potential doctor.

Nonetheless, school activities will probably be more distant for most mature students and so there is likely to be a greater emphasis on community activities or, for graduates, university activities. You may wish to mention any relevant work experience you have gained, together with an explanation of why you have decided to study medicine at this stage.

IN GENERAL

Always bear in mind the possible repercussions of what you write in your personal statement. What you have written in this section is virtually certain to attract at least a couple of questions during any subsequent interviews. The implication of this is that you must only write about things which you will be able to talk about in more detail at an interview. It's very easy – and embarrassing – to be caught out by an interested and inquisitive interview panel.

> **Golden rule:** Never write about a subject on your UCAS form if you won't be able to elaborate on it at an interview.

As you fill out your personal statement, always ask yourself: *'What might an interviewer ask me about this?'* For example, if you write:

> 'I enjoy films and spend many evenings at my local cinema'

you could be asked any of the following general questions:

> *'Tell us about a film you have seen recently?'*
> *'What was the best film you have seen in the last year?'*
> *'Who is your favourite film director? Why?'*
> *'Who is your favourite actor/actress? Why?'*
> *'What is your favourite film genre? Why?'*

You could also be asked a medically-related question, such as:

> *'Have you seen any movies with a medical theme'*
> (examples might include *Lorenzo's Oil* and *Outbreak*), or:
> *'Do you think medical subjects make good movies?'*

The panel could also use this as an opportunity to test your 'social awareness' with such questions as:

'What are your views on film censorship?'
'Do you think there is a link between violence on-screen and in real life?'

Clearly, even a relatively innocuous comment can lead on to a whole range of interview questions. This example serves to emphasise the importance of considering what questions *could* be triggered by the statements you make in your personal statement. Think about this carefully as you fill out the section – for each statement you make, consider the questions it could lead to. You may find it helpful to show what you have written to a teacher, particularly if they are willing to give you a mock interview (see chapter 5).

Declaration

Read the declaration at the end of the form carefully to ensure you agree with it, before signing and dating the form.

After you have completed the form

Once you have filled out the form and checked it thoroughly for any errors or omissions, make a photocopy that you can keep for future reference. If you are invited for an interview, a photocopy is a useful reminder of exactly what you wrote in your personal statement!

You will find a postcard-size acknowledgement card with your application materials and you should complete this and attach a stamp. Check the current applicant's fee and read the instruction leaflet for information about methods of payment. Attach your acknowledgement card and applicant fee to the top of the form with a *paperclip*.

You now need to arrange for a referee to complete the back page of the UCAS form with a reference. School and college students should pass the form and the accompanying documents (including instructions) to the Head, Principal, or other member of the teaching staff as appropriate. After completing the reference section, they will then forward your form to UCAS. Applicants who are no longer at school or college should consult the notes supplied with the form to help in the selection of a referee.

The application form should reach UCAS between **1 September** and **15 December** for entry in the following year. However, if you are applying to Oxford or Cambridge the closing date for applications is **15 October**. It is generally recommended, however, that all medical school applicants should submit their UCAS forms as early as possible. For information about late applications (i.e. after 15 December) consult the *UCAS Handbook*.

Upon receipt of your application form, your acknowledgement card will be returned by UCAS immediately. If you haven't received an acknowledgement within 14 days of handing your documents to your referee, check with your referee to ensure that everything has been submitted.

UCAS will then process your application – this can take up to six weeks. Once your application has been processed you will receive an acknowledgement letter bearing your application number and a record of your chosen institutions. Check this through carefully for any errors. You will also be sent a copy of the UCAS leaflet *Advice for Applicants*, which you should read carefully.

Interviews, offers and rejections

Now begins the long wait to hear whether or not you are going to be called for an interview – this period can stretch into the New Year. Applicants to those medical schools that do not routinely interview may receive a conditional offer directly. Unfortunately, some applicants will not receive any offers or interview invitations. All is not lost, however, as you may still be in with a chance of gaining a place through clearing. For more information on the clearing process, turn to the end of chapter 5.

CHAPTER FIVE

Interviews

The role of interviews in the selection of prospective medical students continues to be a subject of great debate among those with an interest in medical education. Just what *is* the most effective way to predict who is going to make a good doctor five or six years down the line? Indeed, what is the definition of a 'good' doctor? It's perhaps not surprising that there is such a wide variation in the selection processes employed by different medical schools.

For most medical schools, the interviewing of shortlisted candidates is regarded as an important part of the selection process. The interview can also have advantages for the applicant, allowing someone with academic weaknesses on paper an opportunity to compensate for these with the strength of their personality, or at least by giving them a chance to make any extenuating circumstances known to the interview panel.

Conversely, it is possible for candidates who appear strong on paper to talk themselves out of an offer with a lacklustre performance at interview. You should therefore think carefully about your strengths and weaknesses, and decide what strategy to adopt with your applications.

Candidates who are worried about how they will perform at interview can choose to apply to those medical schools that usually make offers solely on the basis of the details supplied on the UCAS form. The UK medical schools that do not routinely interview applicants are:

Aberdeen	Edinburgh
Belfast	Southampton
Dundee	St Andrews

However, you should bear in mind that, although it is their general policy to select most candidates on the basis of their UCAS form, these medical schools may still invite some applicants (e.g. mature students) for an interview.

It seems a pity, though, that many candidates restrict their choices by trying to avoid an interview when, with a little preparation, they need have no fear of an interview. We would strongly recommend that you at least try a mock interview with a teacher, to see how well you can perform, before crossing the majority of medical schools off your shortlist.

Assuming that you are applying to medical schools that do routinely interview shortlisted applicants, how should you prepare for your interview and what should you do (and not do) on the day itself? We discuss below many of the questions you can expect to be asked, and give tips on how to present your answers.

Medical school applicants normally find out whether they are going to be called for interview within a month or so of receiving the confirmation of their application details from UCAS. Some medical schools wait until the New Year and, exceptionally, may wait as long as the following March before making a decision.

Being called for an interview is an encouraging sign, as medical schools only invite candidates with genuine prospects of being offered a place. To be offered an interview means that you have got over the first hurdle, but don't let this make you complacent, as there are more hurdles to come. You now need to concentrate on how you can prepare for your interview so you can give your very best performance.

Preparing for your interview

As the saying goes, practice makes perfect and you should enlist the help of a schoolteacher who is willing to give mock interviews. These are an excellent way to learn how to 'think on your feet' and will also help to boost your confidence. If you can, arrange to videotape your mock interviews so that you can critically assess your own performance – this is also invaluable in making you aware of any irritating habits or mannerisms that you hadn't noticed previously!

You can also prepare for the interview by thinking about the questions you are likely to be asked and how you are going to answer them. To some extent, this will depend on what you have written on your UCAS form. Study your photocopy of this before the interview, to remind yourself of what you said. You should also study the medical school's prospectus carefully to remind yourself what features particularly appeal to you (you are bound to be asked why you have applied for a place there) and to avoid asking questions at the end of the interview which make you appear ill-informed.

Later in this chapter we will discuss some of the commoner interview questions, and again you should put some thought into preparing your own answers for these. As we will also mention later, it is a good idea to keep up to date with topical medical stories, and you should get into the habit of keeping an eye open for any medical news you come across either in the newspapers or on television and radio.

As the day of your interview approaches, make sure you know exactly when and where it is to be held. Allow for any delays so that you can be certain of arriving early. Indeed, if your interview is going to be held early in the morning and many miles away from home, consider travelling there the day before and staying with a local friend or relative, or in a hotel. Alternatively, check with the hospital to see whether they have any rooms available in the doctors' or nurses' residences.

Try and get a good night's sleep before the interview so that you don't arrive feeling (and looking) exhausted. The night before you must avoid alcohol at all costs, and also foods which will linger on your breath, such as garlic, onions or a strong curry. Powerful perfume or aftershave is also to be avoided on the day of the interview itself.

Pay careful attention to your personal appearance – medicine is, after all, a conservative profession and your appearance should reflect this. Interview panels have an aversion to unconventional haircuts, loud clothes and excessive jewellery. For men, a dark suit, white shirt and dark tie are a safe option; for women, a smart suit and blouse. Make sure that your shoes are polished, your fingernails are clean and your hair is tidy.

'Dress smartly so that you feel confident. Look at the interviewers when answering their questions and think before you speak.'

By this stage you should be feeling quietly confident and ready to tackle any questions the interview panel throw at you. On the next few pages, we will go into more detail about what form these questions are likely to take. First of all, though, we should begin with a word of warning:

> **WARNING:**
> Always answer questions truthfully and
> in your own words.

This warning should, of course, be obvious. However, interviewees are sometimes tempted to exaggerate or even fabricate their achievements. It cannot be overemphasised that insincerity and inconsistency are easily transparent and do nothing to impress the interview panel.

Similarly, the interview panel want to hear *your* opinions and not those you have gleaned from a parent, a teacher or even a book such as this! In discussing typical interview questions on the pages which follow, we are *not* trying to teach you model answers to repeat parrot-fashion. Instead, we are trying to give you a framework around which to organise your *own* thoughts when preparing for your interview, so that you can plan how you are going to present your true abilities to their best advantage.

At the interview

First impressions

As you enter the interview room, close the door behind you and walk over to your chair to sit down *when invited to do so* by the panel. You must maintain a professional demeanour throughout the interview. Be aware of your body language and under no circumstances slouch in the chair, yawn or fidget. Everyone going through an interview feels nervous and the panel understands this. Nonetheless, they are likely to become irritated if you let your anxiety lead to distracting mannerisms such as scratching your nose or fiddling with your watch.

'Know what you're going to say, keep talking and don't fidget. It's a feat of selling yourself in as short a time as possible, so be prepared!'

'Be confident and friendly but respectful – members of the interview panel will appreciate this.'

'Relax! Everyone gets nervous but if you can keep calm and express yourself confidently, then you are off to a good start.'

'Be honest, be yourself and relax. Generally, they want to find out more about you rather than to ask taxing questions.'

'Go to the interview with a smile on your face!'

Maintain a posture that makes you appear alert and interested in the proceedings. Sit upright and rest your hands on your lap. Maintain eye contact with the person who is asking you a question or to whom you are replying. Speak up so that you can be heard clearly – this will also make you sound more confident – and appear cheerful. Remember, however, that jokes are out of place at an interview.

Interview panels realise that candidates perform better when they are relaxed, and they will normally use the first minute or two of the interview to help ease the candidate's nerves with some preliminary polite conversation. The panel's chairperson will usually welcome you and will usually introduce the other panel members. You may then be asked an opening question, such as:

'How did you travel here today?'

or:

'Did you have a pleasant journey?'

Make your answer succinct – the examiners don't want a blow-by-blow account of your 400-mile journey by train, how you almost missed your connection at Crewe and arrived an hour late at Euston!

Once the preliminary niceties are over with, the interview will begin in earnest. Before we go on to discuss the questions you are likely to be asked, it is helpful to think about interview technique.

Being interviewed is rather like playing chess, in that you should always be thinking at least one move ahead. This is because skilled interviewers don't simply reel off a list of pre-prepared questions – this would be interminably boring for them, and they could have saved themselves all the hassle of arranging an interview by simply sending you a questionnaire. Instead, interviewers will structure an interview so that it is tailor-made for each candidate by taking two factors into account:

- what they already know about you (from your UCAS form);
- what you say in answering their questions.

What the interview panel already knows about you will usually determine the general thrust of the interview. Someone with poor GCSE results or borderline A level predictions is likely to be grilled about their academic ability, whereas someone who has shown little interest in voluntary work may be asked questions which probe their commitment to medicine. This re-emphasises the importance of preparing for your interview by reading through a copy of your UCAS form and thinking about the questions it might attract.

It is also important to realise that the answer you give to each question during the interview will often determine what you are asked next. Interviewers think on their feet and so should you. By being very careful about how you phrase each answer you give, you can subtly take control of the interview and, to some extent, steer it in a direction of your choosing. This is where practice comes in – there is no substitute for experience when it comes to predicting the flow of an interview. For example, consider the common question:

> 'On your UCAS form you mentioned that you did voluntary work during your summer holiday – can you tell us more about this?'

Imagine that you had seen a number of people with Parkinson's disease during your voluntary work, and that you know quite a lot about this condition because you'd seen a documentary about it. How can you use your answer to try and channel the interviewer's questions in this direction? One way might be with the answer:

> 'During my summer vacation I spent two afternoons each week working at my local hospital, talking with the patients and helping the nursing staff with their tasks. The ward I worked on was for elderly patients, and I had to help some of them with everyday tasks like washing and dressing because they had problems such as Parkinson's disease.'

Ending an answer by mentioning a specific new topic will tempt your interviewer to use this as a link to the next question. If the interviewer takes the 'bait', the next question could well be:

> 'One of the treatments for Parkinson's disease is quite controversial – do you know which one, and why?'

The interviewer is referring to the technique in which brain surgeons try to introduce new cells into an area of the brain which loses cells and leads to Parkinson's disease. The technique is controversial because the cells they inject are derived from human foetal tissue and this can only be obtained following an abortion. This has led to a number of ethical dilemmas regarding how the foetal tissue should be obtained.

By thinking ahead and taking particular care over how you stress each answer, you may be able to influence the direction of the interview until the panel feel that it is time to move on to a new area of questioning. This approach also maintains the flow of the interview and keeps *you* talking – this is important because you don't score any points while the panel are doing the talking. Be careful not to go over the top, however, and waffle on endlessly without letting the panel get a word in edgeways. Say what you need to say and then wait for the next question.

Although the specific content of the interview will vary according to the interviewee, the nature of the questions tends to fall within five general categories, designed to find out more about:

- your motivation,
- your personality,
- your interest in medicine,
- your academic ability,
- your ability to communicate and reason.

Your motivation

Deciding to become a doctor is not a decision to be undertaken lightly and the interview panel will naturally want to know how you came to your choice of career. They are therefore almost certain to ask:

'Why do you want to be a doctor?'

Notice the choice of words – interview panels seldom ask *'Why do you want to study medicine?'* As Stella Lowry explains in *Medical Education*, the phrasing of the question is quite deliberate, because going to medical school is widely regarded as vocational training rather than an end in itself. You should therefore remember that, while interviewing you, the panel are asking *themselves* the question *'Will this person make a good doctor?'* There are three things the interview panel will be looking for in your answer.

First, they will want to know that you reached the decision of your own accord, not that your parents or teachers made the choice for you. Coming from a medical family can be a mixed blessing in this regard. Having parents (or siblings) who are doctors shows that, to some extent, you already appreciate what a career in medicine entails. However, children from a medical background can sometimes appear to be merely drifting into the 'family line' without considering all of the options open to them. Avoid any suggestion, however inadvertent, that your decision is not entirely your own.

Second, the interview panel will want to gain some idea of your personal motivation to study medicine. Interviewees who express a wish to earn lots of money or win the Nobel prize are likely to be rejected outright for being too self-centred or unrealistic in their expectations. At the other extreme, professing a desire to devote your life selflessly to caring for the sick sounds unconvincing and may raise concerns about your ability to make difficult decisions. As with all answers you give at interview, it is usually best to try and strike the middle ground:

'I have always enjoyed the science subjects at school and I would like to have a career where I can maintain this interest. I also enjoy human contact and, having spent the summer holiday working with residents at a local nursing home, I believe I would find working with patients and their problems both challenging and immensely rewarding.'

Third, the panel will be looking for evidence that you have some idea of what a career in medicine involves. As we have just mentioned, children from medical families have a built-in advantage in that respect. There is no denying that training to be a doctor is often arduous and can put tremendous strains on the individual and his or her immediate family. Nonetheless, you should have made an effort to explore what your future career involves. Having said that you want to spend the rest of your career caring for people, it will enhance your credibility if you can provide evidence that you already enjoy doing so.

Anyone considering a career in medicine should involve themselves in voluntary work while at school, in order to find out how suited they are to working with and caring for other people. Take the initiative to apply to a nearby hospital, nursing home or charity to see what they can offer you. Many of these units will have a volunteers' scheme in place and will be glad to hear from you. A one-off visit doesn't really demonstrate a heartfelt commitment to helping others – instead, the interview panel will want to see that you have made a regular effort over a period of time. Don't forget to mention voluntary work on your UCAS form, and if you have done so, be prepared to explain in more detail at the interview exactly what work you did.

Many schools now arrange work experience opportunities for their students – find out if you can spend some time in a local hospital. While you are there, make an effort to speak to those already working in medicine to find out more about what is involved. You could also contact older friends who have already gone to medical school or people you meet during your voluntary work. If you're very lucky, they might be willing to spend time giving you a mock interview!

Having ascertained your reasons for wanting to be a doctor, some interviewers might ask the follow-up question:

'Which medical specialty attracts you the most?'

Very few doctors settle upon their chosen specialty before they have been to medical school. You will have an opportunity to work in most of the specialties as a medical student, and so a perfectly valid answer might be:

> 'As I haven't yet had any direct experience of the different specialties, I can't really say which one interests me most. I'm keeping an open mind for the time being, and I will wait until I've had some experience of each before I make a choice.'

If you have already formed an opinion about what interests you most, be careful about sounding too definite about it. Not only does an open mind sound more reasonable at this stage, you may fail to impress those in the interview panel who don't practise that specialty.

'Try not to set your heart on one branch of medicine too early on – just wait and see.'

Once the interview panel have satisfied themselves about your reasons for wanting to be a doctor, they will want to know why you have chosen *their* medical school as the place to do your training. Be prepared for:

'Why have you chosen this medical school?'

Your choice of medical school will have a profound influence on your future career and indeed, as many people meet their future partners at university, your future life in general. The panel will want to see that you have done some homework and made an effort to explore what their particular medical school has to offer, rather than simply picking them at random. Chapter 3 of this book should have helped you to appreciate the different characteristics of each medical school, but don't forget to read through the prospectus of each medical school on your shortlist and try to contact current students for their advice. A good answer might therefore be along the lines of:

> 'I was looking for a course which integrated clinical medicine with the basic sciences, so that I would be able to see patients from an early stage. After reading your prospectus and speaking to the students who showed me around during the Open Day, I decided that the medical course here is what I am looking for.'

Avoid giving trivial or off-putting answers, such as:

> 'I want to be close to Euston station so that I can visit my girlfriend in Manchester on weekends.'
> 'I've heard this medical school is the easiest to get into.'
> 'The nightlife is very good around here.'

Applicants to Oxford and Cambridge will be interviewed by their chosen college and this should also have been picked with the same care as the medical school itself. These applicants are also, therefore, going to be asked why they have applied to that particular college, and you should prepare an answer accordingly.

Your personality

Throughout the interview the panel will be trying to learn more about your personality, with two questions in mind:

'Know about the course you are applying to do, why you want to be a doctor and why you want to study at that particular medical school.'

'Always read the prospectus on the train on the way to the interview. It can be useful to quote the course details back at the interview panel at appropriate moments – it always impresses them.'

- will your character be compatible with a career in medicine?
- how will you fit in with, and contribute to, the life of the medical school?

The interview panel will hope to see that you are level-headed, with a good measure of common sense. Applicants with unrealistic aspirations are likely to become disillusioned and drop out of the course, and so are unlikely to be made an offer. Similarly, candidates who appear offhand, arrogant or thoughtless will not impress the panel.

In deciding how well you will fit in with the life of the medical school, the interview panel will already have studied your UCAS form and may well ask you about the personal interests and pastimes you have mentioned. Make sure you remember what you wrote on the form, and think about the questions that may be asked in advance. Never try and exaggerate your achievements or make up an interest in a subject you know little about – bluffing is fairly obvious to experienced interviewers, and you'd be surprised how often somebody on the panel turns out to know more about the subject than you!

Even if you haven't listed any interests on your UCAS form, the panel will probably try asking you anyway:

'What do you enjoy doing in your spare time?'

You must prepare an answer for this question to avoid a long, embarrassing silence punctuated only by incoherent 'ums' and 'ers'. Try to avoid listing solitary pursuits (reading, sewing, jogging, etc.) and concentrate on activities which involve teamwork (team sports, drama groups, etc.). The panel will be looking for a well-rounded individual who enjoys interacting with other people. They may be concerned that a 'loner' will lack the social skills necessary to communicate and work with patients and colleagues.

Your interest in medicine

Although you may profess a burning desire to study medicine, the interview panel will want some evidence that you practise what you preach. An effective way of providing this is to demonstrate your knowledge of medical current affairs. After all, what sort of future doctor would have no interest in news stories that are related to their chosen profession?

It's a good idea to get into the habit of reading at least one quality newspaper and one general science journal (*New Scientist* would be a good example) regularly for at least three months before the interview, making a note of any major medically-related stories that appear. Television news bulletins are also a good source of information, as are science documentaries such as *Horizon* and *QED*.

Stories to look out for include:

- medical 'breakthroughs',
- topical controversies,
- ethical issues,
- NHS politics.

The demarcation between these categories is not clear-cut. Nonetheless, they give you a starting point around which to start thinking of questions you may be asked. Obviously, we can't predict what may be newsworthy at the time you read this book. However, we can illustrate what approach you should take by referring to some recent examples.

MEDICAL 'BREAKTHROUGHS'

Medical knowledge normally advances by a series of small steps, but occasionally a significant leap forward is made which attracts the interest of journalists. Examples are the identification of the genetic defects that underlie particular diseases (such as cystic fibrosis and muscular dystrophy) or the discovery of a new treatment to help sufferers of a particular condition.

If a major breakthrough has been widely reported in the press before your interview, there is a chance that you will be given a question relating to it. In general, the interview panel will simply hope to see that you are aware of the issue itself, rather than having a detailed understanding of the science behind it. Even if you are not asked directly about a recent medical innovation, you can draw upon your knowledge of recent stories to illustrate your answers to other questions and impress the panel with your interest in your future career.

TOPICAL CONTROVERSIES

Medical controversies which have made the headlines over recent years include the debate about BSE (bovine spongiform encephalopathy, or 'mad cow' disease) and its possible links with CJD (Creutzfeldt-Jakob disease) in humans, the shortage of donor organs for transplantation, and the role of HIV in the causation of AIDS.

By asking for your views about these controversies, the interview panel is not expecting you to come up with an instant answer. After all, if a solution was that easy, the topics would hardly be major controversies! Instead, the panel will want to see that you are aware of the issues and that you have formulated (and can clearly express) an opinion about them. For example:

'Have you considered how the shortage of donor organs might be tackled?'

> 'It is important that people are aware of the importance of organ transplantation and how it can radically change the lives of recipients. By increasing public awareness of this, more people would hopefully be encouraged to carry donor cards. Another option would be to make organ donation compulsory, allowing people the right to 'opt out' if they object, but this is regarded by some as an infringement of their rights. One might also look into alternatives to relying upon the supply of human organs, perhaps by finding ways of using animal organs instead, although this too leads to yet another area of debate.'

Medical controversies overlap closely with ethical issues and your answers should be structured in the same way. Although *your* opinion is being sought, you should acknowledge that you are aware of other views too. Indeed, a good start to an answer is to outline both sides of the argument before making it clear where your stance lies. This makes it clear that you have considered other people's views and are able to weigh up the evidence before reaching a decision – important qualities for the practice of medicine. It can be risky to express views which appear extreme or unconventional, and this is better avoided – controversial ideas have their place in medicine, but probably not during a medical school interview.

To illustrate this point, consider private medicine which is another ongoing source of controversy. You could be asked:

'Do you think private medicine helps or hinders the NHS?'

Answering this question will test your diplomatic skills to the fullest, as some of the interview panel may have thriving private practices of their own. It is worth outlining both sides of the debate before coming to your own conclusions:

> 'Advocates of private medicine argue that it takes some of the burden off the NHS by taking people who can afford to go privately off NHS waiting lists, leaving more resources for everyone else. Opponents of private medicine respond by saying that NHS waiting lists would not be so long in the first place if consultants spent more time in the NHS and less on private practice. I think that patients should be free to spend their money on being treated privately if they wish, as long as it doesn't disadvantage those being treated under the NHS.'

Further questions on controversial issues might include:

'Do you think infertility treatment should be provided by the NHS?'
'What are your views on tobacco advertising?'
'Should patients having surgery be routinely tested for blood-borne viruses such as Hepatitis B or HIV?'
'What are your views on alternative medicine?'
'Do you think boxing should be banned?'

ETHICAL ISSUES

Ethical issues are not solely the realm of doctors but of society's members as a whole. Questions about ethical issues are a favourite of interviewers, as they test your ability to reason clearly when faced with a difficult decision. They can also be a good opportunity for you to demonstrate your knowledge of current affairs, as the panel will often try to find an ethical issue to discuss which is particularly topical (see above). Some of the commoner topics are:

- euthanasia,
- rationing of treatment,
- *in-vitro* fertilisation (IVF),
- termination of pregnancy.

Questions about **euthanasia** often take the form:

'Is it ever justified to help end a patient's life?'

A widely-debated subject is the difference between killing and 'letting someone die'. Although it is illegal to actively end a patient's life, or to help patients to do so themselves, doctors are not obliged to act to prolong a patient's life at any cost. There are circumstances when to continue the treatment of a patient would be futile or would prolong suffering.

The principle which doctors often refer to is that of *primum non nocere* ('above all, do no harm'), which has its origins in the Hippocratic Oath. Thus it may be justified in certain circumstances to withdraw treatment from a patient even when this will lead to their death. The ethical dilemmas involved in this issue were brought to the fore by the case of Tony Bland in 1993 (see panel).

Some doctors have gone further and have openly admitted to active involvement in helping patients to end their lives. Dr Jack Kevorkian has campaigned in the United States to make physician-assisted suicide legal. He has openly admitted to helping 28 people to die since 1990.

> **Tony Bland**
>
> Tony Bland was a football spectator injured at Hillsborough stadium in 1989. He sustained brain damage and remained in a persistent vegetative state, unaware of and unresponsive to his environment. In 1992 the High Court and ultimately the House of Lords decided that his treatment could be withdrawn. He died in March 1993.

In March 1996 he was acquitted (for the second time) of charges of illegally assisting in suicide by a Michigan court.

The **rationing of treatment** has both ethical and political importance. When the NHS was being set up in the 1940s, it was anticipated that the costs of running the service would be balanced by the savings made through improvements in the nation's health. Such a view now seems hopelessly naïve in light of the spiralling costs of running the NHS. This has led people to consider how health care should be rationed because, with a demand that outstrips supply, not everyone can be offered the care they need. A question on this may take the form:

> *'If two patients need a life-saving treatment, but the NHS could only afford to treat one, how might doctors choose who to treat?'*

'I think doctors would have to consider who was more likely to respond to treatment, as this would be a major factor in the decision. They would also want to think about who would gain most from the treatment, in terms of their life expectancy and quality of life. I am sure this kind of decision is often difficult, and if they felt uncertain about what should be done, then they would probably discuss the options with colleagues.'

Public interest in the issue of when to offer or withhold treatment was heightened by the case of 'Child B', a ten-year-old girl with leukaemia, whose health authority refused to fund further treatment (see panel).

Infertility treatment, and in particular **IVF** (*in-vitro* fertilisation), receives a great deal of publicity because of the complex ethical issues that can arise. Recent issues have included debates about whether there should be age limits for patients undergoing infertility treatment and whether it is ethically acceptable for a man's stored sperm to be used after his death.

Questions about **abortion** often relate to the circumstances in which you feel it would – or would not – be acceptable. For example, if you believe it would be acceptable for parents to request a termination of pregnancy when the baby

'Child B'

In 1995 Cambridge Health Authority decided not to fund the further treatment of a ten-year-old girl with leukaemia who was given just weeks to live. The likelihood of the treatment being successful was thought to be only 2.5%. In court, she was referred to as 'Child B'. The Health Authority's decision was eventually upheld by the Appeal Court. However, an anonymous donor stepped in to pay for private treatment. 'Child B', subsequently identified as Jaymee Bowen, lived another year before dying in May 1996.

has a major congenital abnormality, do you think it would also be acceptable for them to request a termination if the baby was a girl when they preferred to have a boy?

Further questions on ethical issues might include:

> *'Do you think it is right to refuse to treat a patient who smokes cigarettes?'*
> *'How would you respond to a patient who refused treatment for a life-threatening condition?'*
> *'Is it ever ethically justifiable to involve patients in a research trial without their consent?'*

NHS POLITICS

The majority of doctors in the UK work within the realms of the National Health Service and you should be aware of some of the major issues that have concerned the medical profession over the last few years.

'Be aware of current issues, particularly medically-related ones. Think through the type of questions that you might be asked and prepare a framework for an answer.'

The greatest changes in recent years occurred in 1991, with the introduction of the so-called NHS reforms. An 'internal market' was created within the NHS, with health-care providers competing for patients. General practitioners were given the option of taking control of their own budgets (becoming 'fund holders') and were encouraged to 'shop around' for treatment for their patients. Hospitals could also take more control of their finances by becoming self-governing trusts, competing with each other for referrals from general practitioners.

The main aims of the reforms were to improve the cost effectiveness of health-care provision and to improve the service to patients. To see if this is indeed happening, the Government has encouraged audits of spending and performance. In addition, hospital league tables are now published comparing, for example, the waiting time for patients to see a consultant when they are referred by a GP and how long they have to wait if an operation is cancelled.

The **Tomlinson report** (see panel) generated a great deal of controversy when it was published and is most likely to be asked about at interviews for the London medical schools.

The Tomlinson report

This report (named after the committee of inquiry's chairman, Sir Bernard Tomlinson) was published in October 1992. Commissioned by the Government, the inquiry examined the relationship between the NHS and medical education and research in London. The report recommended the merger of eight of the nine London medical schools into four colleges (Imperial, King's, Queen Mary & Westfield and University). In the short term, St George's is to remain free-standing. The report also proposed cutting the number of medical students in London by 150 per year and the devolution of their teaching to general practices and district general hospitals. If the report's recommendations are followed through, London will lose several thousand hospital beds.

You should also be aware of **The Health of the Nation**, a White Paper published by the Department of Health in 1992, which has set out a strategy for disease prevention and health promotion in a number of Key Areas (see panel).

Further questions on socio-political issues might include:

> *'What do you know about Care in the Community?'*
> *'How do you think patients' social conditions affect their health?'*
> *'What are your views on the recent Government reforms of the NHS?'*
> *'Do you think hospital league tables are a good idea?'*

The Health of the Nation

The White Paper identified five Key Areas in which improvements in the nation's health can be achieved:

- coronary heart disease and stroke;
- cancers;
- mental illness;
- HIV/AIDS and sexual health;
- accidents.

The paper sets future targets in each of these areas (for example, cutting cigarette consumption by at least 40% by the year 2000).

Your academic ability

The interview panel's assessment of your academic ability will have a major bearing upon whether they make you an offer and, if so, what grades they set as an entry requirement. This, in turn, will depend upon your track record at GCSE level and, if your school has included it in your confidential report, a prediction of your likely A level results. Questions about your academic ability are virtually certain if you are having to retake your A levels.

The interview gives you an opportunity to put your own case across if you feel that your academic track record has been adversely affected by your circumstances. If so, don't be reluctant to explain this to the panel. Such an explanation will be strengthened by any evidence (letters from teachers or your GP) that you submitted with your UCAS form. In the absence of any single problem which distracted you from your studies, consider whether you simply misjudged the balance between your academic work and other activities such as sport or playing in the school orchestra. The panel may take a lenient view in such circumstances.

Indeed, one reason for interviewing applicants is to give those whose academic records are a little below par an opportunity to explain why, and counterbalance any minor academic deficiencies with their other qualities. However, it should be remembered that the average A level grades of entrants to medical school is ABB and so this is the minimum target to set yourself.

Direct academic questions designed to test your knowledge don't often crop up during interviews unless you're applying to Oxford or Cambridge, where applicants will often be asked questions to assess their understanding and their ability to reason from first principles.

Your ability to communicate and reason

Throughout your medical career you will have to interact with patients and colleagues, and this depends upon your ability to communicate with them effectively. The interview panel will therefore be judging your performance throughout the interview, assessing how well you express your views.

Make sure you answer every question clearly, with no mumbling and as few 'ums' and 'ers' as possible. Take care to structure your replies logically and talk in grammatical sentences, avoiding monosyllabic ('yes' or 'no') responses.

Well-structured answers will also impress the interview panel with your ability to reason. Always think through your replies logically and, when asked for a view or opinion, acknowledge the existence of opposing views as well. This will not only demonstrate your ability to consider both sides of an argument, but also pre-empt any *'Yes, but ...'* retorts from the panel.

'Try to show the interview panel that you are capable of rational thinking. Be able to express views on any topic. Your answer need not be right, as long as there is some logic to it.'

'Dress well, appear confident, and try to show some maturity in thinking.'

Your questions

Most medical school interviews last between ten and fifteen minutes. Toward the end, the panel will invariably ask:

'Do you have any questions?'

This is your opportunity to ask the interview panel a question of your choice, and you should think carefully beforehand whether there is anything you will want to ask them about. However, we recommend that you do *not*:

● reel off a list of half a dozen questions – it will irritate the panel, who will be keen to move on to the next candidate;

● ask about something that is already covered in the prospectus – it will show you haven't done your homework properly;

● ask about something trivial – if you're asking a question just for the sake of it, then don't.

If you don't have anything to ask, it is perfectly acceptable to say:

'Thank you, but all my questions have already been answered by the information in the prospectus and during my tour of the medical school.'

After the interview

Once the panel have finished answering your questions, they will bring the interview to an end by thanking you for attending. They may also indicate at this point how long you will have to wait before you hear whether you are going to be made an offer. Thank the panel before you stand up to go, and then leave the room as graciously as you entered, even if you think the interview went badly. Don't slam the door (accidentally or deliberately!) on the way out.

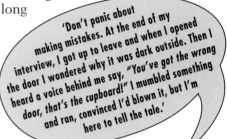

'Don't panic about making mistakes. At the end of my interview, I got up to leave and when I opened the door I wondered why it was dark outside. Then I heard a voice behind me say, "You've got the wrong door, that's the cupboard!" I mumbled something and ran, convinced I'd blown it, but I'm here to tell the tale.'

Once you have left the room, the panel will discuss your performance and decide whether or not they will make you an offer. A variety of systems for grading the candidates exist, but they all do roughly the same thing, dividing the interviewees into three categories:

- those who will definitely be made an offer;
- those who will definitely be turned down;
- those who will be made an offer *if possible*.

Applicants in the last category will be made an offer if, at the end of the interviews, there are some places left and they have been among the strongest applicants within this category.

After the interviews are over, the waiting game begins. This can be a nail-biting time, but you will have to be patient while the medical school informs UCAS of its decision, and this in turn is passed on to you. You will normally hear the outcome within a matter of weeks. Offers can be unconditional or conditional.

Unconditional offers are made to applicants who have already taken their A levels (or equivalent), attained the academic standards required by the medical school, and impressed the members of the selection committee (on their UCAS form and/or at interview) enough for them to want to give the applicant a place. The latter point is very important – three A levels, all at grade A, will not necessarily guarantee you a place at medical school. You will still have to convince the medical school that you possess all the other qualities necessary to make a good doctor.

Conditional offers require applicants to achieve a minimum standard at A level (or equivalent) before they will be accepted. The guide in chapter 3 indicates the typical A level offers made by each medical school in the UK. However, you should note a couple of important points.

First, the offer made will only apply to your first attempt at your A levels. Applicants taking their A levels for the second time will usually be set a higher target to attain, as candidates normally achieve higher grades at their second attempt.

Second, medical schools do not make identical offers to everyone. If a medical school is particularly keen to admit an applicant, they may make them a lower offer than usual. Conversely, a higher offer than normal may be made when an applicant needs encouragement to attain their A level grades. A number of revision guides – such as *Longman A-level Survival Guide*, by Caroline and Ted Wragg (Longman, ISBN 0 5822 9978 0) and *How to Pass Any Exam* by Brian Duncalf (Kyle Cathie, ISBN 1 8562 6237 5) – are available to help you with the planning of your revision strategy.

What happens if you don't receive an offer, either unconditional or conditional? One option is to think very carefully about your choice of a career in medicine and consider whether you should change direction. Think particularly carefully about *why* you may have been turned down – was it, for example, because of your academic record, your interview performance, or a poor report from your UCAS referee?

If you're confident about your choice and still want to try and obtain a place at medical school, two options are open to you, both of which depend upon your performing very well at A level:

- you can try again for a place during the clearing process, after the A level results are announced;
- you could try reapplying the following autumn, once your A level results are known.

Either way, if you haven't been made an offer, it is worthwhile trying to find out whether you will be reconsidered after the A levels results are published. The medical school will probably be unwilling to discuss this directly with you, but may be more forthcoming with your UCAS referee – ask him or her for advice.

Receiving your grades

A level results are announced on the third Thursday in August. If there are any problems with your grades, time will be of the essence, so don't go away on holiday over this period. You may need to telephone around, write letters or even visit medical schools in person to try and secure a place.

MATCHING YOUR OFFER

Hopefully your examination results will be sufficient to meet the conditional offer you are holding. If this is the case, well done – you have earned a place at medical school! Your medical school will also have been informed of your results and will contact you with further information shortly.

THE CLEARING SYSTEM

Medical schools sometimes have a handful of places left unfilled after the examination grades are released. The clearing system exists to help medical schools fill these places, and as a result it may allow you to find a place at medical school if you fail to meet your conditional offer by a small margin. It can also give you a second chance if your grades are good but you didn't receive an offer when you originally applied. However, don't be too optimistic: of the 4235 students who started medical courses in 1995, only 126 (3%) received their places through clearing.

If you missed your conditional offer by a single grade, you may still be in with a chance. Two or more grades below your offer, and your chances of acceptance are virtually non-existent, although there is nothing to stop you making enquiries. Contact the relevant admissions tutors at once to find out whether there are any unfilled places available and if they would be prepared to accept you. Time is of the essence – there will be many others in the same position as yourself, all vying for the few places that may be available.

If you have difficulty contacting the admissions tutor, your UCAS referee may be more successful. It may also help if your referee sends the medical school an updated reference by fax, particularly if your examination performance was affected by extenuating circumstances.

If you didn't receive a conditional offer when you originally applied but you have good grades, get in touch with as many medical school admission offices as possible to see if they have any places available. Act quickly and don't forget that your UCAS referee may be able to help. Your chances of success are slim, however, particularly if your grades are lower than AAB.

Back to square one?

What happens if you've been through clearing but you haven't found a place at medical school this time around? Where can you go from here? The available options include:

- retaking your examinations;
- choosing another course.

RETAKING YOUR EXAMINATIONS

Deciding on this route requires considerable thought and careful introspection. You need to be able to identify the reasons why you failed to achieve the necessary grades first time around, and to be realistic about your chances of improving them at a second attempt. Ask others, particularly your teachers, for their honest appraisal of your abilities. Their advice may be hard to take at first, but in the long run it could help you to refocus your aspirations in a more appropriate direction.

If you do decide to retake some or all of your examinations, find out which medical schools would be prepared to consider you. The attitudes of medical schools towards resit candidates vary considerably, but many will not consider you unless there were major extenuating circumstances to explain your performance first time round. Such a reason might be a significant personal illness (e.g. glandular fever) or the loss of a close relative. Letters of support from your school or GP can prove very helpful if you reapply.

In chapter 3 we identified those medical schools that state an explicit policy towards resit candidates in their prospectuses. Nonetheless, there is little to lose by writing to the medical schools that interest you, to ask if they would be prepared to consider you. Make sure you mention your examination results, any extenuating circumstances that affected your performance, and when you intend to sit your retakes. By identifying which medical schools would not consider your application, you avoid wasting choices on your UCAS form.

CHOOSING ANOTHER COURSE

This will be a difficult decision to make, particularly if your heart is set on going to medical school. However, there are many courses available in subjects that are allied to medicine and which can form the basis of a stimulating and rewarding career. Such courses include Physiology, Pharmacology, Biochemistry and Anatomy.

Having completed a degree course with a good (first or upper second class) degree, you could try reapplying to medical school as a graduate student. This can be a very difficult route into medicine, but some do succeed.

CHAPTER SIX

Preparing for medical school

Achieving the necessary examination grades to be accepted at medical school may seem like the final hurdle, but in fact it just marks the beginning of a whole new series of challenges to come. The first of these is to prepare for the transition from school to university.

In this chapter we will discuss two of the most important things to think about before you start university – accommodation and money. In addition, we will say a little about joining the armed forces, as this is something a number of students consider before and during the medical course.

Accommodation

Many universities have a policy of trying to provide their own accommodation for all first-year students. The prospectus will contain details of the availability of university-owned accommodation at your medical school. Regardless of their policy, contact the university's accommodation officer as soon as you know you have achieved the required grades, to check whether you will be given a room or, failing that, what they can do to help you find somewhere to live. If you want (or have) to live out, you may also find help and advice at the students' union.

Don't forget that you may need to budget for gas, electricity and water, depending upon where you live. Many full-time students are exempted from Council Tax, but you may become liable under certain circumstances – for example, sharing a private house with non-students. For accurate and up-to-date information, check the situation with the local council in the area you intend to live.

Money

Medical education is expensive, not only for the government (which spends around £150,000 per student) but also for the students (who currently leave medical school with an average debt of £3696). Things are likely to get even worse: it has been estimated that the recommendations of the Dearing report (see box) could leave UK medical students with an average debt of £20,000 by the time they qualify.

'Don't buy books until you arrive at university. Someone will usually be able to sell them to you second-hand.'

It's therefore essential that you sort out your finances as far as you can before commencing your medical course. This means not only arranging your sources of funding, but also opening a bank account and ensuring that you have adequate insurance cover. A list of useful sources of information about financing your way through university can be found on pages 170–1.

Grants and fees

There have been many changes in the funding of higher education and student grants in recent years, but some of the most significant changes will result from the so-called Dearing report.

At the time of writing, details of how the report's recommendations would be implemented were still being debated and it is still unclear precisely how medical students will be affected. Nevertheless, it does seem certain that students starting their courses from 1998 onwards will face a completely new set of rules with regard to fees and funding. There are two proposals in particular that merit a mention at the present time:

MAINTENANCE GRANTS

The Dearing report has recommended that maintenance grants be abolished. In 1996–7, maintenance grants were worth over £2000 a year for some medical students.

Loans will take the place of maintenance grants, although the report has acknowledged the special position of medical students who face a much longer course than most university students. There are, therefore, proposals to make government-funded bursaries available to help assist medical students during their courses. No details of these bursaries are currently known, but more information should be available following the

> ### The Dearing report
>
> A major new report into the future of higher education in the UK was published on 23 July 1997. Titled *Higher Education in the Learning Society*, the 1700-page publication is more widely known as the Dearing report, after the committee's chairman Sir Ron Dearing. Although the report looked at many different aspects of higher education, it is the recommendations for changes in student funding that have attracted most attention.

publication of a government white paper, *Lifelong Learning*, in the autumn of 1997.

TUITION FEES

All universities charge fees for registration, tuition, examinations and (where appropriate) graduation. Until recently, UK residents obtaining a place at university were normally eligible for an award to cover their university fees. All this has changed with the publication of the Dearing report. The proposed plan is for students to make a contribution towards their tuition fees by paying an annual fee of around £1000.

The payment of tuition fees will be means-tested, making allowance for students from low income families. Students whose families earn less than £16,000 a year will not have to pay tuition fees, whereas those from families earning over £34,000 a year will have to pay the full £1000 fee. A sliding scale of charges is likely to apply between these income groups.

Whom you contact for further information depends upon where you live. Funding for students from England, Wales or Northern Ireland is administered by their Local Education Authority (LEA), and you should contact your LEA at an early stage for further details. Funding in Scotland is administered by the Student Awards Agency for Scotland (SAAS).

The rules regarding European Union (EU) nationals and non-UK/non-EU residents were unknown at the time of writing.

Student loans

The role and/or scope of student loans may change as a result of the Dearing report's proposals. Student loans were originally introduced by the government in 1990 and are administered by the Student Loans Company. They were often used to supplement the maintenance grant but, with this grant's abolition, may now become a central element of student funding.

Student loans are not means-tested. Interest is charged at an annually-adjusted rate that is linked to inflation. You will normally receive details on applying for a student loan when you take up your place at medical school.

> A leaflet containing details of the student loans scheme may be requested from:
>
> Student Loans Company Limited
> 100 Bothwell Street
> Glasgow G2 7JD
>
> ☎ 0800 40 50 10
>
> WWW http://www.slc.co.uk

Access Funds

For students running into serious financial difficulties, Access Funds have traditionally been a potential source of additional funding. How (or even if) these funds will be affected by the Dearing report is not yet known. Around £23 million was made available to publicly-funded colleges in 1996–97 for this purpose. Access Funds are administered by the colleges themselves and the colleges decide which students to support with payments and how much payments should be. Ask your college for further information.

Other sources of funding

Some trust funds and charities give support to students. You may be able to find a list at your local or medical school library. Awards from these bodies are often made for specific purposes (e.g. purchasing equipment or funding travel abroad) and often only specific individuals are eligible (e.g. those born in a certain area or whose parents work in a certain profession).

Your medical school, college or university may have hardship funds or scholarships for some students – ask for details. Some students may be eligible to receive support from the Department of Social Security (☎ 0800 666 555) or the Council – make enquiries to the relevant department.

Bank accounts

Regardless of your sources of income, a bank account will be a virtual necessity and you will find a number of banks and building societies vying for your custom. Shop around for the most attractive deal you can find, bearing in mind such practical points as the proximity of branches to where you will be studying and the availability of cash-dispensing machines.

Insurance

Make sure you have adequate insurance cover for your personal effects, particularly if you have a television, hi-fi or computer in your room, or if you have a bicycle. First of all, though, check whether you are already covered by your parents' home contents insurance.

Student Life: A Survival Guide, by Natasha Roe (Hobsons Press, ISBN 1 8532 4827 4) is a useful general handbook.

The armed forces

A number of medical students consider joining the armed forces at some point during their medical training. You can only enrol for a cadetship after you have reached the clinical phase of your training and are within three years of graduation. Nonetheless, you may apply for further information at any time before this.

Royal Army Medical Corps

Students can join the Royal Army Medical Corps (RAMC) via a medical cadetship. Cadetships are open to both male and female students. To be eligible, you must be within three years of sitting your final examination and have completed your training in the basic medical sciences, enabling you to commence a course in clinical studies in a recognised medical school.

For three years you can be paid as a second lieutenant with no obligation to undertake Army work or military activity until you have completed your pre-registration year. Your commitment is to serve in the Army for a Short Service Commission of six years from the date of joining for duty as a fully registered medical practitioner.

Further information on medical cadetships in the RAMC may be obtained from:

Officer Recruiting
RHQ RAMC
Keogh Barracks
Ash Vale
Aldershot
Hants GU12 5RQ

☎ (01252) 340307/9

Royal Navy

Full cadetship, holding the rank of Surgeon Sub-Lieutenant, is awarded on or after obtaining the Second MB examination (or equivalent). An application for a naval cadetship may be made six months before examination. A Short Career Commission of six years' service commences at the date of full registration or the date of entry, whichever is the later.

Further information on cadetships in the Royal Navy may be obtained from:

Office of Dean of Naval Medicine
Monckton House
Institute of Naval Medicine
Alverstoke
Hants PO12 2DL

☎ (01705) 768107   Fax (01705) 504823

Royal Air Force

The Royal Air Force offers careers to male and female doctors. Women in the medical branches receive the same professional and service status and pay as their male colleagues. The RAF awards cadetships to students in the clinical part of their training and within three years of graduation.

Cadetships lead to Short Service Commissions (SSCs). You will be able to opt for either three or six years' service, which does not commence until full registration with the General Medical Council is obtained. Those who require General Professional Training may only apply for a six-year SSC.

Further information on service in the Royal Air Force may be obtained from:

Royal Air Force
Careers Information Office
Kelvin House
Cleveland Street
London W1P 5FB
☎ (0171) 636 0782   Fax (0171) 436 1707

CHAPTER SEVEN

The medical course

The integrated medical course – what to expect

Integration means that the courses you will study are arranged as far as possible to complement each other and make learning and understanding easier for the student. For example, when learning about respiration you will learn simultaneously about the structure of the lungs (*anatomy*), how oxygen gets into the body and carbon dioxide is eliminated (*physiology*), the cellular processes which lead to energy production from oxygen (*biochemistry*), what diseases may affect the lungs (*pathology*) and how bacteria invade the lungs (*microbiology*). Clinical visits to the hospital wards will allow you to meet and to talk with patients with lung disease (*'take a history'*), you will be shown how to examine a patient to elicit important clinical signs (*clinical examination*) and you will see the results of simple investigations like X-rays.

This seems such a logical approach that you may well ask why it has not been adopted before. The most likely reason is that it is administratively convenient for the university departments to work in isolation in the traditional way: anatomy of the chest (*term one*), physiology of respiration (*term two*), biochemistry (*term three*), pathological processes (*term four*), microbiology (*term five*), clinical examination (*term six*), ward attachments (*term seven onwards*). As you can see, the same syllabus is covered but, in the traditional approach, the subjects are presented in a series of unrelated topics, while the integrated approach looks to be more student- (and learning-) friendly.

A typical week in your first term at medical school

Week One is devoted to Freshers' Week: a few days to settle down in your new surroundings, familiarise yourself with the campus and city layout and, most important of all, make a whole network of new friends. You will have a great time! Make the most of it, because the work starts soon.

After this, you will soon settle into a daily routine of lectures, seminars, presentations, visits to the library for research material, laboratory-based practicals in pharmacology, physiology and biochemistry, communication skills exercises, small-group teaching and many other sessions. At some universities, you may find that you share some lectures with students from other faculties such as nursing and pharmacy. Look upon this as another opportunity to expand your social circle.

Every course will be organised differently, but table 7.1 will give you some idea of what a typical week might include.

Table 7.1

MONDAY

Communication skills
role-playing exercise in small study groups

Physiology practical
practical on cardiovascular physiology

TUESDAY

Anatomy
lecture on the structure of the heart

Physiology
lecture on the control of heart rate and blood pressure

Public health & epidemiology
lecture on the epidemiology of heart disease

Professional skills
afternoon workshop on ethical issues in medicine

WEDNESDAY

Clinical experience
visit to a local General Practice

THURSDAY

Physiology
lecture on endothelial cell physiology

Pharmacology
lecture followed by practical on drugs that affect the heart

FRIDAY

Ward visit
bedside teaching in examination of the cardiovascular system

Private study
afternoon spent writing up practical and preparing essay

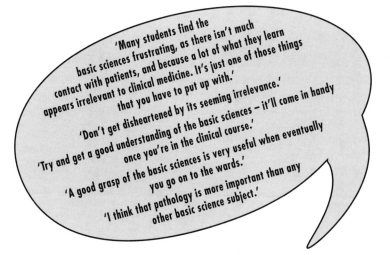

'Many students find the basic sciences frustrating, as there isn't much contact with patients, and because a lot of what they learn appears irrelevant to clinical medicine. It's just one of those things that you have to put up with.'

'Don't get disheartened by its seeming irrelevance.'

'Try and get a good understanding of the basic sciences – it'll come in handy once you're in the clinical course.'

'A good grasp of the basic sciences is very useful when eventually you go on to the wards.'

'I think that pathology is more important than any other basic science subject.'

Teaching and the university

There is no doubt that education *can* be a thoroughly boring time for all concerned. Good teaching makes a big difference. You will have met good teachers already – they inspire you with a love of the subject, an infectious enthusiasm, and a desire to master their subject. There is quite a difference between school and university. Your school teachers were trained to teach; most lecturers are recruited for their research capabilities and may have little experience of, and almost no training in, teaching methods. Universities are trying to put this right with teaching improvement programmes and monitoring standards through student feedback and appraisal. Even so, you may still come across university staff who see teaching as a most unwelcome distraction from their research.

Most medical schools have well over 100 students in each year of training, some more than double this. This presents difficulties for teaching, so the lecture forms the basis for a lot of the teaching at medical school. The lecture has been described as the process by which information from the notes of the lecturer are transferred to the notes of the student without going through the mind of either.

To be fair, various efforts have been made to replace the lecture, to make the learning experience more enjoyable and less of a chore. Group discussions – variously called seminars, small-group teaching or tutorials – are popular with students and teachers alike.

A 1st year medical student

'My life as a first year medical student is, not surprisingly, centred around the study itself. The first few weeks of medical school were for me, and, I presume, for others, a time of great change, making new friends, settling into student life.

The anxiety passed as I settled into a routine that brought with it security and a certain sense of independence. Small sixth-form classrooms have now given way to lecture theatres and the student-teacher interaction has changed to student-centred learning. All in all quite a transition, but for the better I feel.

One of the subjects I was most looking forward to was anatomy and I was not disappointed. Though slightly morbid, this was the first real chance of being able to see what I had learnt in theory. It is also this subject that gives you an almost cult-like status among your housemates who expect to find dissected limbs in the freezer. It is also these same housemates who come to you for a cure for their aches and pains after your first week at medical school.

Because my medical school is situated in the hospital itself, away from the main campus, medics tend to be isolated and socialise together. This allows you to make friends quickly and we often go for a night on the town together.

After the first couple of months of the medical course it is still somewhat difficult to imagine actually becoming a doctor, but up until now medicine has definitely been the right choice for me.'

You will notice that the sample timetable (table 7.1) has quite a variety of presentations; though several of the modules could be in lecture format, teaching staff are now trying to introduce different ways of conveying information. Some subjects do lend themselves to large-scale teaching, but to achieve things like the attitudinal objectives of the GMC requires

'During the basic sciences course there are phenomenal amounts to read, but you learn to pick and choose.'

'Don't go to the ends of the earth to get to every lecture, but make sure you copy up any you miss.'

'If you've missed lectures, borrow the notes of a friend and fill in any gaps (which most often you will notice the day before an examination!). The trouble you go through to look things up when you've missed them will encourage you to listen carefully and write down important facts only.'

alternatives such as small-group teaching, seminars, projects and discussion groups. Group discussions are ideal opportunities to test and develop critical thinking and the application of factual information to problem solving. Feedback is instant and difficulties with understanding in the individual or in the group are soon identified.

Learning support

At long last, medical schools are acknowledging what generations of students have long recognised: lectures are great as a means of 'covering' a syllabus for a mass audience, but little of the information 'delivered' is retained by even the most attentive student. Most lectures are too long and try to achieve too much in the allotted time.

Most schools are at last becoming educationally aware. There is now considerably less emphasis on didactic teaching and more on finding ways to facilitate learning. You will notice references in the prospectuses to *directed self-learning* (Aberdeen), *self-directed learning* (Leicester) or *this encourages students to develop their own learning strategies* (Manchester). You should regard this as a good thing, a definite 'plus' for the course, because it means that you take responsibility for your own studies, within a planned timetable. It also recognises that there is a difference between teaching (something the teacher does) and learning (something the student does)!

You will be pleased to know that universities are taking great strides forward at facilitating learning, employing a combination of the tried and tested with the innovative.

The tried and tested includes the well-equipped **library** which all medical schools enjoy. All subscribe to a huge range of medical journals covering all the major and most minor specialties, and most will acquire a specific non-stock item for a student project.

Computer facilities are usually impressive. Aberdeen has computer classrooms and Southampton has clusters of computers for casual use at sites across the whole campus. Networked PCs with access to E-mail and the World Wide Web are common, as are Medline, JANET (**J**oint **A**cademic **NET**work) and BIDS (**B**ath **I**nformation & **D**ata **S**ervice), information retrieval systems you will soon become familiar with. All of these are useful for obtaining references for reports and projects. If you have limited experience of computing, you will soon learn all you need to know – whether this is using a statistics package, designing a database or simply word processing – often because some courses include computer-based exercises within them. There are usually lots of photocopiers around but they tend not to be cheap.

In the innovative category are self-paced teaching aids, which include tape-slide programmes, learning guides, self-study booklets, self-assessment exercises and video and audio tapes. Computer-aided learning applications are improving quickly and CD-ROM interactive teaching materials are now available for a wide variety of topics. Some of these packages are excellent, and provide the student with superb graphics and complementary text, as well as clear and precise notes. As more software becomes available, the investment in this type of learning material will increase markedly. Sheffield, Nottingham and Dundee draw your attention to their investing heavily in dedicated suites for computer-assisted learning (CAL).

Tomorrow's Doctors places great emphasis on the acquisition of practical skills which you will need as a doctor. Learning these skills takes time, patience and practice. Until recently, all of the essential basic procedures were performed on patients; with students on the low point of the learning curve, this was sometimes an uncomfortable experience for both parties. It was not always convenient to practise on patients, so alternatives had to be found. Dundee is particularly proud of its custom-built clinical skills laboratory, allowing students to achieve a degree of proficiency before trying 'the real thing' on patients. A Medical Skills Learning Facility is opening at Aberdeen and other universities will be developing similar units in the near future.

Logbooks record which conditions and investigations students have seen, assisted with or performed during the clinical attachments. They provide a checklist of common problems and diseases which ought to be seen at least once, and include records of:

- satisfactory attendance on emergency receiving days;
- post mortems attended;
- case presentations made.

This logbook system is open to abuse, and the essential procedures listed may be taken as a *minimum* for passing the course. It is being introduced widely, but the details will be quite specific to the medical school.

The **post mortem** room is not the most friendly environment in which to learn medicine, yet pathological demonstrations can teach us a lot about the way disease affects the body. Technology has come to the rescue at Aberdeen and elsewhere in the form of closed-circuit TV, which allows remote demonstrations of organs at autopsy. This is a much more satisfactory method of clinico-pathological teaching because *(a)* the pathology department is often in a fairly remote part of the hospital, and *(b)* your olfactory organs are not challenged!

Poor teaching is the death of learning. Universities are making great efforts to improve the quality of teaching and are utilising technological advances wherever possible. This does make the life of a medical student much more interesting and the medical course much more challenging and enjoyable than trying to master isolated facts through sheer force of memory.

Vacations!

First, the good news. Term or semester dates for most medical students in the first couple of years of their course are more or less like those of all other students, with long Christmas and Easter recesses and a summer break that

A 2nd year medical student

'I always have a nine o'clock lecture. You can always spot the medics at this time in the morning – they're the only students up! During today's lecture 180 sleepy second years faithfully reproduce what seems like a few thousand acetates from the projector. At the moment we have a very full timetable with lectures from nine until five every day.

I am a regular at the medical school coffee bar, even frequenting in between lectures for a caffeine boost. This is necessary to keep your brain working at the lightning pace of the physiology lectures. The coffee bar is also the social epicentre of the medical school and a visit is guaranteed to provide a laugh.

We often have seminars along with biochemistry and microbiology laboratory classes. We also go to timetabled patient contact teaching sessions. We have GP and hospital ward attachments where we practise skills such as history-taking and examining patients. These provide that metaphorical 'carrot in front of the donkey', reminding us that all the study enables us to practise as a real doctor.

In the evening I do a couple of hours' work. Most lectures only provide you with an outline of a subject and it is necessary to do some wider reading in order to understand it more fully. Later I go to the pub. This is always full of medical students (they're the loud ones!). Then I may go on to a club or an organised medics' event. We're very sociable creatures – sleep is only allowed at the weekend! Of course, if you do additional activities (I'm involved with the theatre) you don't sleep then either. The next morning I usually go for a swim. The course is so intensive you can't afford to waste a second!'

gives you plenty of time to swan around Europe, earn some cash or have a good time at home. The bad news is that in the later years of the course, when your clinical exposure increases, the vacations are much shorter. It's tough being a medical student if you are a holiday animal.

Full details may be found in the prospectus; check them if you must, but they are hardly a factor in selecting a medical school. To take Southampton as an example, expect:

- normal Christmas, Easter and summer vacations in Years 1 and 2;
- two months' holiday at the end of Year 2;
- Year 3 is 42 weeks long;
- Year 4 is 38 weeks long;
- Year 5 is 48 weeks, due to much longer clinical attachments.

'Enjoy those three-month holidays! Participate in extracurricular activities and make as many non-medic friends as you can.'

'You may find that you have a lot of "free" time. Don't waste this. In the same note, don't go crazy over loads of work. It is important to strike the correct balance.'

'Enjoy! Take advantage of the clubs and societies, because in the clinical years you will have less time and are tired more, due to the early starts.'

'Make sure you take advantage of all the opportunities at university because there's not as much time afterwards.'

'Life will never be so easy again, so have a fantastic time and don't stress!'

Early clinical experience

There is nothing like a break from your studies when you are beginning to realise just how much there is to learn. Early patient contact comes as a welcome break from the classroom, but there are other benefits too:

- it reminds you that you are training to be a doctor;
- it helps consolidate some of the more esoteric information you will be learning;
- it helps relate indigestible facts to real-life situations;
- it lets you see the impact of disease on patients and their families;
- it lets you see what being a doctor really entails.

Many courses stress that clinicians take an active part in the early years. While this is largely true, the amount of time allotted to clinicians varies a lot. Check out the prospectuses carefully if you are the type who relishes the idea of getting away from the lecture theatre to see patients early in the course.

Visits to hospitals and to general practice form part of basic sciences training in most medical schools. These visits often continue throughout the basic sciences course, because talking to and dealing with patients and their relatives takes lots of practice. You will not have mastered these by graduation, but you will be sufficiently skilled to become a competent pre-registration house officer.

In Sheffield, students work with patients regularly from the first term onwards: the Family Attachment Scheme allocates a student to a GP and to a family which is about to experience a birth; and the Street Medicine Course and the Ward Attachment Scheme are part of the first-year course, giving students the opportunity to see medicine at close quarters. Bristol, Nottingham, Newcastle, Leeds and several others also advocate early and frequent contact with patients.

Your first visit to a hospital ward or a general practice will be informal; later you will visit to talk to patients, later still practise examination of the heart and circulation in normal subjects (your fellow students!), learn about heart disease, then visit the wards to interview and examine (under supervision) patients with heart problems, and discuss these with the clinical tutors. In some universities, you may make some kind of presentation to your

A 3rd year medical student

'I'm currently doing my research work for a BMedSci and, for once, I don't have to wake up early every day. I can always turn the alarm off, go back to sleep and start work in the lab later on during the day – preferably just before lunch!

Working in the lab is an interesting and enjoyable experience. We spend some time designing experimental techniques and testing out our ideas.

The lunchtime breaks tend to be longer in the third year. It is the only time during the day that we can all get together and socialise. We sometimes have our meal at the local pub or attend a lunchtime lecture given by one of our supervisors.

In the afternoon, I carry on with the lab work or spend some time in the library searching for references. We often have our afternoon break with the PhD students, discussing their ideas. At the end of the afternoon there is sometimes a meeting with our supervisor, who tries to remind everyone of the seriousness of our work. He's unsuccessful . . . while he's talking about cytokines and antibody levels, we're making plans for the evening.

After dinner we either watch TV, go to the movies or gossip with our housemates. After that some work gets done.'

fellow students. These visits will complement your teaching and boost your confidence, so that when you become a clinical student, you will quickly form part of the medical team.

Some schools attach less importance than others to patient contact in the early years of training. Oxford and Cambridge are predominantly academic courses, with little patient contact until much later in the course.

The clinical course

Clinical teaching methods

Clinical teachers may be invited to help with basic science teaching, especially in those parts of the course where integration has been achieved. They too are not usually trained teachers, but they will try to help you see the relevance of the basic sciences to clinical medicine. They will enjoy being asked lots of questions about patient care.

Much of their contribution comes later, when clinical studies form the predominant part of the course. Small-group and bedside teaching is the norm. You will also be able to learn by attending outpatient clinics and seeing how doctors communicate both good and bad news to patients at first hand. This is more an *apprenticeship* approach to learning. You will learn about common clinical problems from talking to patients, examining them, discussing various aspects of the diagnosis and their care with the medical staff, and reading up about them later.

Pick up any textbook on medicine and you will understand how anxious students can become in the clinical years. Deciding what you should learn requires guidance. To some extent, logbooks do help with this, but Dundee has gone further by providing print-based and electronic **study guides** to help your self-directed learning. Leicester provides detailed learning objectives to define what students should be able to achieve by the time of graduation. Look out for these in the prospectus of any university you might want to apply to.

Linking basic sciences and clinical medicine

While integration is the name of the game, several universities try to provide a formal bridge between the basic sciences and the clinical years. This largely involves learning how to talk to and examine patients to establish a diagnosis: this is called *'taking a history'* and *'clerking a patient'*. It usually comprises a modular course dedicated to focusing on acquiring clinical skills, just before going on to the wards on a full-time basis. It may go by one of several names. Nottingham has an Introductory Medicine and Surgery course in the third year, Southampton calls it a Clinical Foundation Course, and Edinburgh an Introduction to Clinical Medicine. Edinburgh also has

Clinical Correlation modules throughout the first two years, to relate the preclinical sciences to patients.

Clinical aspects

Leaving the lecture theatre behind and heading for a full-time attachment on the medical wards is quite a landmark in medical training. You haven't finished memorising facts, but at least you are seeing patients every day, learning to talk to and examine patients, visiting outpatient clinics, attending ward rounds and getting the feel of life as a doctor. Most students are ready for a change at this stage. The basic sciences course can seem to last a long time, especially when the relevance to medicine of some of the subjects seems obscure.

Most students will have had some visits to the wards during basic sciences. Now your time on the hospital wards increases and you will have the opportunity to see patients every day. The idea of clinical training is to build upon your early but brief experience with patients and to help you develop the skills you will need to become a doctor.

Life is much more varied and interesting at this stage. The daily routine in a busy hospital is very different from the relaxed environment of medical school. There are outpatient clinics to visit, operations in theatre to observe, ward rounds to attend. How illness affects patients and how patients cope with illness is fascinating. This part of the course should provide you with the stimulus to read about the medical problems patients present with.

Most medical schools expect students to produce a **case report** on a patient, which will require following up a patient after discharge from hospital. Students often find this an enjoyable experience, as most patients are not at their best in hospital due to their illness, so it is helpful to see how complete a patient's recovery might be. Some illnesses, however, do have a devastating impact on a family. While this can be upsetting, it is important to be aware that some patients' problems begin when they are discharged home.

What to expect

The clinical attachments are generally referred to as 'clerkships': you learn to 'clerk' a patient, which simply means that you will try to ascertain as much as possible about each patient by talking to them about their medical problems (finding out what their *symptoms* are) and then examining them for *signs* of disease. You will find this difficult at first –

'The clinical experience is what it's all about! You'll never have felt so humiliated/embarrassed/stupid/useless in your life, but it's brilliant! (Particularly when you go on a ward round and know the answers to questions that your 5th year colleagues do not!)'

'Be prepared to be embarrassed, humiliated and to get grilled by the consultants. If you're of a sensitive nature, change! You will find it stressful if you take all the consultants' remarks to heart.'

everyone does – but with practice you will soon get
the hang of it and after a while it becomes
almost second nature.

Of course, the purpose of all this is to find
out why a patient is ill. This is a much
harder objective to achieve. You will be
taught the basics of how and why
symptoms develop, how to find out which
symptoms your patient has, how to examine
your patient, how to make sense of the information you have gathered to
help you establish a diagnosis. This is the most challenging part of clinical
medicine.

'The first full clinical year is the year where you feel like you are completely useless and that you are in the way. But hang in there! During the second clinical year, things should begin to fall into place.'

A 4th year medical student

'Getting up in the morning becomes difficult in the fourth year, especially when you know that you have to dress smartly and prepare for action. Then you make your way to hospital in order to attend whatever has been timetabled: a ward round, a clinic, a theatre list or even a teaching session. The former and the latter are an opportunity for the senior staff to quiz, embarrass and remind you that there is only a year or so to go before your first housejob. All fourth-year medics are expected to be omniscient both in the basic and clinical sciences, for example knowing all the enzymes of the TCA cycle as well as the 145 recognised causes of finger clubbing.

Five o'clock usually marks the end of a busy day in hospital and unless you are stuck in a clinic or theatre with an over-enthusiastic consultant, or you are on take, you make your way home with only one thing in mind: *What to have for tea?* The menu is usually limited and the choice is made quite easily.

Going up to your room brings back bad memories of the preclinical years and it is not long before you aimlessly turn the book pages trying to assimilate more facts and avoid further ward round massacres.

Perhaps the most important event in the life of a fourth year takes place afterwards: a visit to the local pub for a pint or two and a discussion of current affairs (= gossip) with your friends.
Another exciting day in the life of a fourth-year medic is thus concluded. For anyone thinking that we aren't serious enough, just wait until next year!'

You will have support and help from your colleagues and your supervisors, the medical team to which you are attached. Although some clinicians enjoy a fierce reputation, you can be reassured that most will remember how difficult things can be in the early stages of a clinical attachment. By observing how skilful the medical staff are at presenting just the right amount of detail to convey an accurate picture of a patient at the time of admission, you will soon learn which features of an illness are of immediate, and which of a lesser, importance for making the right clinical decisions. You will practise your history-taking skills and present patients to the other doctors on ward rounds so that you too can refine your technique. By the end of your clinical attachments, as you prepare for your first housejob, you will be fairly accomplished.

Clinical attachments

The length of each attachment will be dictated by the number of students and the number of hospitals and wards available to the medical school. Below is a list (by no means exhaustive) of some attachments you might expect:

Accident & emergency	**Haematology**
Anaesthetics	**Health care of the elderly**
Cancer medicine	**Neurology**
Cardiology	**Obstetrics & gynaecology**
Child health	**Ophthalmology**
Dermatology	**Orthopaedics**
Ear, nose & throat	**Palliative care**
General medicine	**Psychiatry**
General surgery	**Radiology**
Genito-urinary medicine	**Rheumatology & rehabilitation**

Emphasis throughout is on developing clinical and practical skills, reinforcing the knowledge acquired during the early years and learning about disease, its impact on patients, families and society, and its treatment in the widest sense. Those in complementary medicine often accuse doctors of being too specialist or of not being 'holistic'. As you will discover during your training, there is a close inter-relationship between social, psychological and physical aspects of illness which the caring doctor cannot ignore.

Your tutors will have specific targets for you to achieve by the end of your clinical training. First, you will be expected to take a history from a patient with symptoms of heart, lung, gut or neurological disease and then:

- elicit common signs *(examining the patient)*;
- make a working diagnosis *(what is wrong with the patient?)*;
- make a brief 'differential' diagnosis *(what else might it be?)*;
- make a plan of investigation *(what tests need to be done?)*;

- consider aetiology (*causes*), pathology and principles of treatment.

Daily routine

During your attachments in medicine and surgery, your programme will be fairly flexible. This stage of training is intense and the work fascinating and enjoyable. The idea of the clinical part of the course is to build upon the basic sciences and to allow you to learn more about patients and their diseases.

The best way to do this is almost literally to hang on to the house officer's coat-

'Never be afraid to do something new (as long as you are well supervised). I found my best experiences were when I was chucked in at the deep end. For example, the first time I performed cardiac massage, I was ordered to do it by the consultant, and as it was an emergency situation I couldn't make excuses so I just had to cope and do my best.'

A 5th year medical student

'Almost every day we have to be at the medical school by nine o'clock in the morning. There is usually either a ward round, an out-patient clinic or a theatre list that we are expected to attend. On ward rounds we have to present patients that we have clerked. We try and sound confident even if we don't know much about the patient's condition, hoping that the consultant won't ask a question that we cannot answer. In the clinics we try to stay awake, especially towards the end, and hope that the doctor will teach us something. In the operating theatre we have two important roles to fulfil: to assist the surgeon and to tell jokes in between operations. Sometimes during lunchtime there is a lecture or seminar that we are expected to attend. However, the attendance is not always impressive. Otherwise, lunchtime is a chance to socialise with other students and staff.

In the afternoon we sometimes have bedside teaching in which we hope that we will not be humiliated for our examination skills. Otherwise, we go on to the wards and clerk patients. It is always enjoyable to take the history and examine patients, trying to work out what is wrong with them. However, if assessments are close then we often disappear into the library in order to do some work. We usually get home at five o'clock. After dinner and rest, we do some work. However, there is always time for sports, the cinema, the pub or a night club, especially following a difficult set of examinations.'

tails. Wherever the house officer goes, you should go too (the job of the house officer is described fully in chapter 11). This means that you will see all there is to see and be available to help out wherever you can. This might mean taking blood samples from a patient, say, or putting a cannula (or fine tube) into a patient's vein to give drugs, or fluid, straight into the bloodstream. This is a good time to refine the practical skills you may have learned at first in the medical skills laboratory. The house officer will probably teach you how to adapt your technique when things don't go as planned!

'In the operating theatre, I never knew whether to try and make intelligent conversation with the surgeon, or just to keep quiet and thank my lucky stars that he wasn't asking me any questions!'

You will have the opportunity to observe at first hand how patient problems are sorted out. There is a daily routine of sorts for you and the house officer: checking each patient every day, adjusting their drug treatment, organising assessment by the occupational therapist or physiotherapist, making arrangements for discharge, going 'on take' to admit acutely ill patients according to the duty rota.

Life in hospital is rarely without event, so be prepared to take off in pursuit of the house officer at a moment's notice, most often in response to a cardiac arrest bleep. Be prepared to get involved. Once you have learned the skills of cardiopulmonary resuscitation, your skills will be very helpful to the members of the cardiac arrest team, whether this is by getting access quickly to the bloodstream to deliver drugs, pressing on the chest to keep the circulation going or keeping the patient oxygenated by artificial respiration.

You should spend some time with the on-call medical team who look after all patients admitted as an emergency. This will teach you to:

- cope with acutely ill patients and their relatives;
- get used to working long hours;
- get used to thinking when tired;
- work as part of a team.

You will also make your first trips to the operating theatre. It will all be somewhat confusing to start with, and you will have trouble making things out as you peer into someone's abdominal cavity. After a while, it begins to make sense and you will enjoy assisting with simple operations such as removal of the appendix and holding retractors (these keep organs out of the way so the surgeon can see clearly) during bowel and gall bladder surgery.

Teaching methods

Clinical and bedside teaching is a particularly interesting facet of the course. Here, you learn to listen to patients, how to examine patients properly to elicit physical signs of illness which point towards a diagnosis, and how to think quickly so that you consider several diagnoses but reduce these to just one or two possibilities. Teaching at this stage is predominantly in small groups of about four students; this can be intimidating at first, especially if you are a little shy or if you are used to large-group teaching. Being in a small group is an ideal way to learn quickly as it's fairly obvious to the teaching staff if the message has not got across.

'Clinical students have to be self-motivated as frequently there is no formal teaching but it is up to them to find a patient to take a history from and examine. At this stage you get out as much as you put in. If you stick with it, your confidence on the wards and around patients increases.'

'I was too polite at times and didn't ask for teaching and as a result I missed opportunities. Most people want to teach ... they are flattered by your interest but are unlikely to offer their services if you don't ask.'

'The only way to learn is to ask around and see what's happening. If you're interested, show your enthusiasm and you'll be roped in.'

'All doctors like friendly and interested students.'

Most clinicians enjoy bedside teaching. You will soon see that they often have 'favourite' patients they have known a long time, probably because the medical history is quite complicated. These sessions are a good opportunity to see how you are progressing compared with your fellow students. You may find too that some clinicians are on the look-out for potential future house officers. Many recruit those who have been students on their firm, so do your best to show how skilful and knowledgeable you are!

Special study modules in the clinical course

One advantage of the liberalisation of medical education is increased freedom for each student to have a greater say in the design of the training programme and the opportunity to study personally-selected subjects in greater depth. This may range from short projects lasting a week or so early in the course to three-month special study modules in the later years.

Special study modules (SSMs) are a recent introduction in line with the recommendations of *Tomorrow's Doctors*. The core curriculum is designed to prepare students for the house officer year, but SSMs are designed to broaden the student's outlook and to allow some choice in the direction his or her studies take. Medical schools are still coming to terms with the concept of SSMs, but in time about a third of the total undergraduate programme will be made up of SSMs distributed at intervals throughout the course. Glasgow already allocates 20% of the undergraduate programme to SSMs, Cardiff 30% and Dundee 33%.

Suppose one of your particular interests is in heart disease and you wish to spend some time gaining more experience in this field than was possible during the regular clinical attachment. What you get out of this module really depends upon what you want to put in to it. A sample programme might be as follows:

OUTPATIENT CLINICS
Attend specialist cardiac clinics.
See and assess patients with cardiac symptoms.
Discuss diagnoses with medical staff.
Arrange appropriate investigations.
Observe investigations such as: treadmill test, cardiac catheter,
echocardiography, 24-hour heart rhythm monitoring.

CORONARY CARE UNIT
Learn management of heart attack and rhythm problems.
Assist resuscitation team when appropriate.

CARDIAC SURGERY
Observe procedures such as: heart valve replacement, coronary artery bypass
surgery, coronary artery balloon angioplasty, pacemaker implantation.

VISIT TRANSPLANT UNIT
Observe cardiac transplantation and its after-care.

CASE STUDY REPORT
A patient with severe heart failure being assessed with a view to heart
transplantation.

Student support

Leaving home, family and friends can be a traumatic experience. Not
everyone makes the adjustments that are a necessary part of coming to
university easily, so there are various forms of support available to try to deal
with problems that may arise. First of all, you will be assigned a personal
tutor who is there to give advice, mainly on academic matters, but who is
also available to help with non-academic problems. Every university will
have a counselling service to help sort out specific worries in confidence, and
an advisory service may be run by fellow students
around the clock to try to deal with problems that
cannot wait.

'Working with patients can be very emotionally demanding, and there is no hiding from the sometimes disturbing realities of life. But there are also some wonderful characters and great comic moments.'

Other forms of help may be available. For
example, Nottingham has a *mentor* system in
the clinical years to make sure that students
who are having specific difficulties during the
clinical attachments have someone outside the
medical firm to contact. Southampton students in
the second and third years act as tutors for new entrants to the school to
provide help and encouragement.

Being a student is supposed to be a fun as well as a learning experience.
You should feel confident that, whatever the problem, there are experts on
campus who can help.

Studying abroad

Bristol pioneered the European Credit Transfer Scheme and other universities have followed suit by permitting students with a working knowledge of, or an A or AS level in, a foreign language to undertake part of their training in Europe.

If this applies to you, and the prospect of some time abroad appeals to you, it makes sense to keep up your language skills by attending out-of-hours tutorials or the language laboratories of the university. These courses help to provide a cultural and social background to the country to be visited.

Up to ten Manchester students spend part of the fourth or fifth year in France, Germany or Switzerland. Bristol students may spend up to three months abroad. Cardiff *'particularly welcomes applications from students who offer a European language as one of their A level subjects. Opportunities to participate in European exchanges exist within the medical curriculum'.*

European programmes are also being developed elsewhere. Schools without European links will often offer the chance to travel during the elective periods. Because courses are evolving, recently-introduced changes may not have reached the prospectus – it might impress to seek clarification at the interview. If the European experience appeals to you, you can be reassured that any time spent at an approved European centre will be recognised by the GMC.

One point to remember: check whether a specific code number is required on the UCAS form if you intend to apply for this type of course. If you are not successful in your application because of limited numbers, you will be considered automatically for a conventional non-European course so, if it appeals to you, you really have nothing to lose.

Summary

A few years ago, you would have had little choice in the type of course on offer. With few exceptions, you would have spent the early years in a lecture theatre or practical class before spending the remaining years walking the hospital corridors. Schools are now making determined efforts to change their courses in line with GMC recommendations.

You should spend some time thinking about the type of course which might appeal to you the most. The traditional course is predominantly an academic one, much like any other university degree course, and has limited or no contact with patients in the first few years. The newer 'integrated' course means that you will have contact with patients early in the course (from week one in some schools) through clinical demonstrations in the lecture theatre, in the hospital wards, at the general practitioner's surgery or in the community.

Didactic teaching is being replaced by a wide variety of teaching and learning methods. Students are being given greater choice in designing a course which appeals most to them. It has never been a more exciting time to be a student.

CHAPTER EIGHT

An intercalated degree

During your early undergraduate training, the range of subjects you will study is broad. It is inevitable that you will enjoy some more than others. You will find a few particularly interesting and you may regret that the core medical curriculum does not have the time to allow you to develop your interests in one particular field further. Special study modules, discussed in chapter 7, were recommended by the General Medical Council to allow you to gain more experience of particular fields that are of interest to you.

Most universities go further and offer students the opportunity to suspend their medical training for a year to study one area in much greater detail. Typical examples of areas of study include:

- a laboratory-based project to examine how blood platelets are affected by aspirin and other drugs, and how this might be useful in patients after a heart attack;
- a clinically-based project to assess whether the amount of information given to patients prior to an operation affects the speed of their recovery afterwards;
- a community-based project looking at the incidence of certain diseases within the local population and how this may be related to their housing or lifestyle.

Whatever the project, the aim is to undertake original research into your chosen topic. As well as writing up your work in the form of a dissertation, you may be able to publish your findings in a medical journal.

This is an intercalated degree. Once you have completed this degree, you can resume your clinical studies, though you will be a year behind your colleagues who started medical school with you (and so they will become medically qualified ahead of you).

WHAT AN INTERCALATED DEGREE ENTAILS

Generally speaking, you will attend a variety of interdisciplinary courses aimed at giving you a thorough understanding of the theory behind your selected area of study, as well as teaching in experimental methodology and statistics. These will help you when you are designing and carrying out your own in-depth research project. The culmination of a rather busy year is the writing up of your dissertation. Your course work and thesis will be submitted to the University Academic Board for consideration for the award of a Bachelor's degree with Honours.

ADVANTAGES OF AN INTERCALATED DEGREE

For students who may be contemplating an academic career, the intercalated year provides a good foundation in research methodology and statistics – useful skills for interpreting reports in the literature. The project work will be rewarding and will teach you to work and think independently. You will be able to pursue your interest in investigative technology or a particular clinical problem, and you may find yourself working under the supervision of clinicians and scientists who are acknowledged experts in their field. As it affords an opportunity to set aside the mandatory components of the syllabus for a while and to pursue an area of particular interest, your additional year should be very rewarding.

'Research is certainly valuable and I am very glad to have done some "real" science, but there is a price to be paid. At most universities it means doing an extra year, which costs money and delays starting the "real" medicine.'

'An intercalated degree is useful if you plan on going into research in the future.'

'Think carefully and speak to others who are doing one/have done one.'

'Do it if you can afford it!'

DISADVANTAGES OF AN INTERCALATED DEGREE

If you look at doctors' qualifications, it is easy to see that most have lots of letters after their names. You should not underestimate how much *effort* is required to earn these.

When you arranged the funding for your medical course with your LEA, you probably declared that your course was going to be five years long. You will therefore need to sort out additional funding as soon as you can with your LEA. Some medical schools offer scholarships, but you will probably have to compete for these.

The intercalated degree is usually between the second and third years. You may find it more difficult to maintain friendships with your course colleagues whose schedule will become more hectic as the clinical component of the course begins.

'It sounds soppy, but friends are important and you get each other through the tough times. If you intercalate you move down a year so they graduate before you, but you can make more friends with another year.'

IMPORTANT THINGS TO KNOW ABOUT AN INTERCALATED DEGREE

It is obvious that the first requirement for consideration for an intercalated degree is that you must have achieved a high standard of examination results during your medical studies. Although you will have a supervisor to advise you, you will need to be highly motivated.

You will add an additional year to the duration of your medical training. Glasgow is unusual in offering a one-year intercalated degree in the Faculty of Medicine leading to an Honours BSc (MedSci) and a two-year course in the Faculty of Science leading to a BSc with Honours. While this may not be important to a student being funded by the LEA, any self-funding student may find this particularly difficult to justify unless there is a real prospect of winning a scholarship.

Not every student will wish or be invited to take another degree. At Newcastle, 10–15% of students choose to read for the Honours degree of Bachelor of Medical Science. Leicester estimates that 10% of students will take an intercalated degree. Cardiff offers places to 15–20% of students but is keen to offer more. About 50–60% of students at some of the London schools take an intercalated degree.

'I now wish that I had done an intercalated BSc. The extra year and the opportunity of intensive research appeals, as does the BSc.'

AN INTERCALATED DEGREE AS AN INTEGRAL PART OF THE MEDICAL COURSE

Exceptionally, an intercalated degree may be part of the standard medical course and so cannot be avoided! The course offered at Nottingham features a research project undertaken in Year 3 which contributes to a Bachelor of Medical Science (BMedSci) degree.

Oxford and Cambridge students read for a Bachelor of Arts (BA) Honours degree in their third year, prior to proceeding to the clinical school. The range of subjects is wide and may include a non-medical subject – refer to the appropriate prospectus for further details. Imperial College School of Medicine is planning a six-year course, incorporating an intercalated degree.

STUDENTS WITH EXCEPTIONAL ABILITY

It is sometimes obvious to academic staff that certain students have a flair for, and show particular promise in, the field of research. In selected cases, a student may be offered the opportunity to delay their return to the medical course and proceed to a combined MB-PhD programme. This option is available at several schools, including Newcastle, Leeds and Leicester. It should be pointed out that the number of students who are invited on to this type of programme is very small, because only exceptional students are considered and the course is lengthened to over seven years.

Finally

You should not let the availability of intercalated degree courses unnecessarily influence your choice of medical school. While they do attract some students, remember that your aim is to qualify as a medical practitioner. If, however, you are interested in undertaking an intercalated degree once you are at medical school, it is important that you discuss your ideas with your mentor or a member of the appropriate academic department. Many departments will have research proposals of their own available, reflecting the interests of the lecturers, but most will be accommodating and prepared to listen to your ideas.

The elective period

The elective period has been a popular feature of the medical curriculum for many years and forms a part of *every* clinical course. The duration of the elective period varies markedly between medical schools, however, as is apparent from table 9.1.

There is also some variation in the nature of the elective period. At Aberdeen, for example, two elective periods are taken. One of these is devoted to a project on a medical topic and is usually taken abroad, while the other allows students to study a non-medical topic (such as a language or business skill) that may be useful in their professional life.

Most medical schools have just one elective period, taken in the final year of the course. The majority of students go abroad, often to countries in the developing world. There is plenty of scope for inventive and original plans, however, subject to the approval of your medical school Dean.

To plan a successful elective period you need to:

- plan ahead;
- take good advice;
- obtain sufficient funding;
- avoid falling ill!

PLAN AHEAD

Electives require advance planning – you can't just hop on a flight out of Heathrow and turn up on a hospital doorstep in Kuala Lumpur expecting to be welcomed with open arms. Exactly how far ahead you need to make plans will depend largely upon where you want to go, but it's not a bad idea to reckon on at least one year of preparation.

Apart from deciding *where* to go (see below), you will need to ask if you will be welcome and arrange arrival and departure dates. You will also need to find enough money to cover the cost of your trip and arrange travel, accommodation and insurance cover. You are also likely to need a course of immunisations (depending, of course, on where you go) and, as it can sometimes require a course of immunisations over several months to achieve immunity, this also needs sorting out well in advance.

Table 9.1 Duration of medical schools' elective periods

Medical school	Duration
University of Aberdeen	2 × 8 weeks
Queen's University, Belfast	6 weeks
University of Birmingham	2 months
University of Bristol	5 + 9 weeks
University of Cambridge	*see below
University of Dundee	10 weeks
University of Edinburgh	16 weeks
University of Glasgow	2 × 4 weeks
University of Leeds	10 weeks
University of Leicester	8 weeks
University of Liverpool	12 weeks
University of London	
Imperial College	12 weeks
King's College	11 weeks
The Royal Free Hospital	8 weeks
St Bartholomew's & the Royal London	8 weeks
St George's Hospital	9 weeks
UMDS (Guy's & St Thomas's Hospitals)	8–10 weeks
University College	10 weeks
University of Manchester	8 weeks
University of Newcastle	9 weeks
University of Nottingham	10 weeks
University of Oxford	*see below
University of Sheffield	10 weeks
University of Southampton	8 weeks
University of St Andrews	see Manchester
University of Wales	8 weeks

*The duration of the elective periods at Oxford and Cambridge depends upon where the clinical course is undertaken.

Don't waste time or put things off, therefore. It's only too easy to realise that you've left your preparations too late and have to settle for a disappointing elective when, with a little forethought, you could have arranged a valuable and memorable experience.

TAKE GOOD ADVICE

Deciding where to go for your elective period is often difficult, which is not surprising when you consider the bewildering array of options available to you. How should you make your choice?

Sources of information about elective periods are scarce – it's not as though you can simply make your choice from a travel brochure. It's very important, therefore, to take advice from others who have already taken their elective. Speak to as many people as possible to find out where they went and how useful and enjoyable they found it. Students often have to write a report for their medical school on returning from their elective, and these are often filed for future inspection by others. Ask the undergraduate office at your medical school if they have any elective reports you can look at.

Another reason for seeking advice from others is that electives are frequently arranged through the help of a mutual contact. You are more likely to be accepted at an institution if someone known to them has recommended you. The consultants in your hospital will often have contacts abroad and may be willing to put in a good word for you – don't be afraid to ask for their help.

What factors do you need to consider in making your choice? First and foremost, you need to choose an elective in a place where you will be safe. Indeed, your medical school Dean is unlikely to approve your elective plans unless he or she is satisfied that you won't be putting yourself in undue danger. You may learn a lot of medicine in the middle of a war zone, but your Dean is unlikely to let you go.

Your Dean will also want to see that your elective will make a significant contribution to your medical education. This brings us on to the question of what sort of experience you wish to gain. Would you like to go abroad or stay in the UK? Do you want to work in a hospital, a research unit or the community? Would you rather spend your elective in the developed or the developing world? Are you interested in a particular specialty or research project?

Most students restrict their choices to places where English is widely spoken. If you're proficient at a foreign language, however, you may be able to consider a wider range of countries. In addition to the elective period, an increasing number of medical schools now include the opportunity to study at a European medical school during part of the medical course, and sometimes up to a year can be spent abroad.

Places visited on electives have included:

- Stanford University, California, to study cardiology;
- the Caribbean, to perform research into sickle-cell anaemia;
- India, to work in a paediatric hospital;
- Australia, to work with the Flying Doctor Service;
- NASA in the United States, to study aviation medicine;
- the *British Medical Journal* in London, to study medical journalism.

If you are going abroad for your elective, your main aim should be to see how medicine is practised in a different environment. However, you shouldn't neglect the more general benefits of travelling abroad. Make sure you include enough leisure time in your schedule to allow you to explore the region and experience the culture. Many students add a week or two of holiday at the end of their elective to allow time for travelling further afield.

Having narrowed down your options, you need to consider some practicalities. Do you know anyone who you can contact at the place you want to visit, or can anyone give you an introduction? How will you get there? Will you need a visa or an immunisation certificate? Where will you stay – is student accommodation provided, and will you have to pay for it? Can you afford to go?

It's essential to get in touch with the centre you wish to visit at a very early stage to make your intentions known and to ask for advice. It's very frustrating to have planned everything down to the last detail only to find that they're already fully booked with elective students and don't have room for you.

'Do something different, something which is not covered in your course. Also, go somewhere different. Broaden your horizons.'

'Despite the temptation to have a complete holiday, it is well worth finding out about a different culture and health care, as well as adding to your own experience.'

'Go as far away as possible and try things you never dared before. It'll be the time of your life if you let it.'

OBTAIN SUFFICIENT FUNDING

Electives can be expensive. Planning things well in advance should give you an opportunity to raise sufficient funds for your trip. Draw up a budget, accounting for:

- travel costs (airline tickets, rail tickets, etc.);
- visas;
- accommodation;
- food and drink;
- leisure activities;
- insurance cover;
- miscellaneous expenses.

You will need to consider how much you can save from your income and, if necessary, how much you can afford to borrow. Your medical school may offer elective bursaries or an elective prize for the best elective report. Look out too for competitions organised by companies (e.g. student travel firms). You could also try writing to your old school or college to ask if they have any travel funds available for ex-pupils – this can be a surprisingly successful way to obtain additional funds. Pharmaceutical companies are not, by and large, willing to provide support for individuals taking an elective.

AVOID FALLING ILL!

You may want to study tropical diseases on your elective, but that's no reason to turn it into a practical experience by catching one yourself. Your risks of falling ill will clearly depend upon where you're going, and once again good advice is essential.

Compile a list of all the countries you intend to visit, *not forgetting to include stopovers*, and find out all you can about the diseases prevalent in those areas. Your general practitioner or your university's student health service will be a good source of advice and should be able to discuss immunisation with you.

In addition to immunisation, there may also be practical measures that you can take to reduce the risk of infection (such as sterilising water or using mosquito nets). By finding out all you can before you go, you will be able to take anything you need with you. Talk to others who have visited the same places and consult up-to-date travel guides. You should also contact the doctors you will be working with in the country itself and ask if there is anything you should bring with you.

Make sure you have adequate insurance cover to help you out if the worst does happen and you fall ill abroad. This is particularly important in North America, where the cost of medical care can be astronomical. If you are going to work in North America you may also require indemnity cover – ask the centre you intend to visit about this before you go.

CHAPTER TEN

Examinations

You will no doubt work hard to achieve the grades at A level or Highers necessary to secure a place in the medical school of your choice. If you do consider yourself blessed with the ability (denied to most) to obtain high marks with no or little effort, be aware that, as a medical student, the quantity of knowledge you will be expected to be familiar with, master and then memorise is huge. If you feel that you have had enough of examinations, read no further – you ought now to consider seriously whether your application to medical school is the right thing for you.

Why examinations are necessary

Being a student is fun. This is especially so for those (let's call them 'Arts' students) whose academic burden is much lighter than medical students', so lectures impinge little on their usual rather hectic social programme. Medical schools long ago devised a strategy to make sure that students abandon their non-academic and more entertaining extra-curricular activities, at least temporarily: they simply publish a timetable of examinations in alarmingly close proximity to significant social events such as Christmas and Easter.

This doesn't mean that university staff have no sense of fun. It's just that medical courses are closely monitored so that standards are maintained nationally. It is because the General Medical Council is charged with monitoring course structure, content and qualifying examinations. This is the result of various Acts of Parliament, a Royal Commission and several Committees of Inquiry into medical training.

From an educational standpoint, examinations are meant to serve several purposes. First, they assess the effectiveness of teaching in reaching objectives set for students. Second, they provide feedback to the student to determine what material has been mastered and what has not. Third, they determine if changes of teaching methods or materials are necessary.

In reality, most examinations force students to get round (finally) to studying course material. This is probably not unreasonable, but with suitable planning, described below, the impact of the education process on other student activities can be minimised.

Examinations in medical school

Ask any doctor over the age of 40 how the medical course ended and he or she will recall the legendary marathon of 'Finals'. This somewhat perverse system was an organiser's dream. All examinations were condensed into one frantic fortnight of essays, *viva voces* and clinical examinations. This fearsome process was looked upon as much as a *rites de passage* as an assessment process. For most candidates, Finals was a nightmare.

Fortunately, many medical schools have evolved from such neolithic times and have either abandoned the Finals examination or reduced both the quantity of examinations and their individual importance. *Continuous assessment* is educationally more acceptable as it offers the candidate the opportunity to remedy weak areas of knowledge which 'Finals' examinations do not. Batches of examinations at the end of each academic term, or at intervals during semesters, may seem like continual *harassment* to some, but it is preferable to discover problems during rather than at the end of a course. Interim assessments of this kind should put examinations in perspective – they are learning opportunities for our future doctors rather than major barriers to progress.

From an educational point of view, it is more appropriate to encourage the development and retention of knowledge and skills through progressive or continuous assessment than to devise one final assessment which relies on short-term memory.

Types of examinations

Many universities are reviewing and changing their examination methods. Essay-style papers have largely been replaced by other forms of assessment which are less stressful on candidates and examiners alike. Many medical schools are tending to favour computer-marked assessments which are more objective, so avoiding examiner prejudice and bias.

The usual approach is the **multiple-choice question** (MCQ) paper, where candidates determine whether questions are true or false. Just to make life interesting, there is often 'negative marking' – get an answer right and you gain a mark; get an answer wrong and you lose a mark. This may seem unfair, but it is important to inhibit guessing (would you want your doctor to guess at a diagnosis?).

Prior to taking your first MCQ assessment, your lecturers will take you through the procedure of completing the answer sheet correctly. This rehearsal is important and you must not miss it. If you have not tried this sort of examination before, it does require a little thought and practice. The ideal strategy, of course, is to work steadily during the term and learn course material well for the examination. Successful students usually think this preferable to learning for the re-sit.

Assessments are not exclusively examination-based, as increasingly **project work** may be set. In some universities, project work may account for 50% of the total marks. This is good news: while you can't throw away your favourite fountain pen, you won't need to fill it quite so often. In your project, you may be expected to demonstrate evidence of self-directed learning, the use of Information Technology to retrieve information, literacy, and analytical, critical and presentational skills.

Other assessment methods currently in favour include:

- short answers of perhaps three or four lines only;
- short essays of about two pages;
- assignments on various aspects of a specific disease;
- oral or poster presentations to small groups;
- *viva voce*;
- data interpretation;
- problem-solving exercises;
- practical work in the laboratory.

Clinical assessments

The assessments you can expect in the clinical part of the course are very different. They are designed to check your ability to:

- obtain medically-relevant information from a patient ('taking a history');
- examine a patient;
- organise and interpret tests such as X-rays or blood tests;
- look after patients safely.

Ultimately, you are really being assessed to see if you are making progress towards becoming a competent and caring doctor.

Other assessment methods include written **case histories** which give you the opportunity to study patients in considerable detail. You will have to read widely, so that you can convince your tutor that you fully understand all aspects of your 'case'.

It is important for you as a medical student to acquire all the practical skills you will need when you are a house officer. This may be assessed informally on the hospital wards by a senior doctor. However, many medical schools have adopted a more formal method with the **objective structured clinical examination** or 'OSCE'. Here, you may be presented with a variety of patients, volunteers or models and asked, for example, to demonstrate how you would examine the heart for a murmur or show how you would listen to someone's lungs.

As a monitor of your progress, many medical schools expect you to keep a **logbook** or record of all the practical procedures you have carried out (such as putting up an intravenous drip or recording a heart trace), the emergency admissions you have seen, and the case presentations you have made at seminars and on hospital ward rounds. The logbook system has several limitations and is undoubtedly open to abuse, but it is very much in vogue.

It is important for you to appreciate the physical, social and psychological effects of illness and to improve your understanding of the contribution of the various health professionals who care for patients. Some schools arrange for you to follow up a patient you have seen in hospital and to observe a patient for several weeks after discharge from hospital. Your report will form part of your clinical assessment.

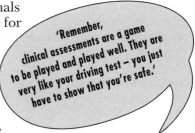
'Remember, clinical assessments are a game to be played and played well. They are very like your driving test – you just have to show that you're safe.'

As in A levels, whatever the method of assessment, you will be fully informed of the way each unit of the course will be assessed.

What if you fail an examination?

All medical students have the ability to pass their university examinations (otherwise they would not be admitted), but occasionally they do lack application at the appropriate time. Most sixth formers will have to think hard about the last time they failed an examination. The shock of seeing an 'F' grade against your name in any examination hits hard. It's not the end of the world, though it may seem so for a while.

If you do fail an examination, remedial work is now the norm to bring students up to the necessary standard – a much more satisfactory solution than being sent down. There are obvious reasons for this. Doctors are expensive to train so 'wastage' has to be minimised. University boards will usually give you one opportunity to redeem yourself through a re-sit. Your revision may be supervised but, if it is not, ensure that you understand why you failed and concentrate on your weak areas. One major disadvantage of a re-sit is, of course, that you will have to revise to ensure that you pass the second time while you are trying to deal with new material from current courses.

If you revise inadequately, the reasons for failure are obvious. If you are unsure of course material, finding out *after* the assessment is too late. If you study hard, a failure may be unexpected – it is essential to swallow your pride and see your tutor to find out what needs to be done.

Learning strategies

No one gets through A levels without discovering a few tricks on how to learn. It is satisfying and often useful if you can work problems out from first principles, but there are times when you have little alternative but to commit material to memory. You may already have developed several learning strategies which help you to learn. You will have plenty of opportunity to put these into practice.

Your lecturers will provide you with a reading list. Check out these in the university bookshop and buy the book which looks the most readable. If you buy secondhand from a more senior student, make sure that you have the correct edition. Some material you will simply need to learn through rote, so you need to use various memory tricks – mnemonics can be particularly helpful.

It is also important that you attend practical classes, as these are often intended to reinforce theoretical material, especially where the concepts may be a little difficult.

After an examination, you should be given feedback fairly quickly – sometimes even the same day for a computer-marked assessment like multiple choice. You should check your own answers as soon as possible – this is an essential part of the learning process.

'Use the course objectives to direct your last-minute cramming. Don't think you are the only one who has not got a clue.'

'Find out what's important and what's not, because more likely than not you'll end up burning the midnight oil learning the latter instead of the former.'

'Be careful about question-spotting. It is much safer to start revision in plenty of time and to cover everything thoroughly.'

'Having done endless examinations up to now and with only Finals left, I still have no idea how best to revise!'

Learning difficulties

There are many reasons why students fall behind with their work schedule. If you are having problems coping, the first thing you should do is decide if you are giving yourself enough time to read your own notes and any handouts you have been given, whether you have omitted assignments designed to help you to understand certain aspects of a module, or whether your social calendar may be at fault. If you are certain that none of these apply to you, there are always people around to talk you through problems (whether these are academic or personal) and try to get things sorted out.

There are several sources of support at university. A personal tutor will be available if you are having academic difficulties. Social or personal problems can interfere with studies, and confidential

'Try not to get too stressed about revision and examinations.'

'Examinations are horrible. Just take one day at a time. Try not to work on a Sunday – go walking, skiing, singing or anything to get away from everyone else.'

'You'll be OK, but there is so-o-o much to learn it can be scary. But hey, if I can do it, so can you!'

counselling, advisory and welfare services are widely available to help. In addition, students themselves often run 'night-line' advice services.

Postgraduate examinations

Medical school provides basic training to equip you for the first step on the ladder as a doctor. The medical degrees of Bachelor of Medicine and Surgery are now regarded as basic qualifications, insufficient for the modern-day doctor, so you will need to continue your studies to acquire further advanced qualifications.

While you will spend a lifetime learning, you will spend several years *after graduation* acquiring the skills needed to allow you to specialise in a particular field. Do not expect to complete your examinations until you are about 28 and don't expect to stop learning until long after that. You will be expected to keep your knowledge up to date through a process of *continuing medical education* (CME). As a hospital consultant or general practitioner, you need to attain a set number of hours of CME each year and you may gain *credits* for attending conferences, clinical meetings or reading professional journals.

Which qualifications you try for depends upon the specialist interest you have and the career you wish to follow. More information about career options can be found in chapter 12. Would-be general practitioners, as well as taking the examination of the Royal College of General Practitioners, often take other qualifications such as the Diploma in Child Health or Family Planning Certificate.

If you want to put letters after your name, you can end up with a fine collection by being a doctor. A few common postgraduate degrees are:

MRCP	Member of the Royal College of Physicians
FRCS	Fellow of the Royal College of Surgeons
DCH	Diploma in Child Health
MRCOG	Member of the Royal College of Obstetricians and Gynaecologists
MRCPath	Member of the Royal College of Pathologists

Those who are inclined towards an academic career may submit a thesis to achieve the qualification of Doctor of Medicine (MD) or Doctor of Philosophy (PhD).

And finally

It is simpler and less stressful to accept examinations for what they are: an irritating but necessary fact of medical student life. Remember that you cannot expect to qualify as a doctor if you do not acquire the knowledge that your teachers (and the General Medical Council) expect. This means that there are times when you will have no choice but to knuckle down and commit to memory enough information to convince your teachers that you have acquired sufficient knowledge to pass on to the next stage of training.

Get used to examinations. The concepts in medicine are no harder than those you have come across in your A level courses. You will need to get organised because you will need to commit some material to memory. The secret is to work smart as well as hard. Resolve not to fail by learning thoroughly and revising properly, and especially in good time.

CHAPTER ELEVEN

Housejobs

Once you have graduated, your carefree student days are over. Hopefully, you will have happy memories of your undergraduate years. Now, for the first time, you are permitted to put your medical degrees after your name – your reward for five years of hard work. Your new title of 'Dr' carries some weight – but also some important responsibilities.

The General Medical Council keep a list of all doctors: the General Medical List. They will send you a *Certificate of Provisional Registration*. This means that you are allowed to practise medicine but only under the supervision of a senior doctor. If you complete this year satisfactorily (as almost all do), you will receive a *Certificate of Full Registration*.

Supervision is necessary because it has been recognised for many years that the five-year undergraduate course does not prepare you sufficiently to work independently, and further training and experience with senior doctors are essential. No matter how much you learn in your five years at medical school, you will find that you need both knowledge *and* experience to become a safe, effective and competent doctor.

The **pre-registration house officer** (PRHO) year is meant to round off your basic medical education and to give you valuable practical experience. You will make an important contribution to the work of the medical team, but this does not mean that you will simply be another pair of hands. Time is set aside for your continuing medical education, a process that will continue until you retire.

Generally speaking, you will work in hospital for the house officer year, six months of which will be in a medical specialty (it really doesn't matter which one, because you will see the full range of medical emergencies) and the second six months in a surgical specialty (ditto). Some hospitals are experimenting with modifications to this, such as an attachment to general practice for four months, but these are the exception at present.

Choosing your house officer posts

By the time you qualify, you should possess adequate knowledge, consultational, analytical and diagnostic skills, and appropriate attitudes to allow you to contribute to patient care. As the aim of the house officer year is to develop you into an independent medical practitioner, it is fair to say that what your seniors will expect of you and the duties you will have are very similar wherever you work.

As you approach the time when you are looking for a job, you will hear a lot of myths about the house officer year – such as that you must work in a teaching hospital and on a professorial unit if you are going to 'get on' in medicine. These are nonsense. Don't discount any job just because it is not in a major teaching hospital. In fact, many district general hospitals will give you the right balance of experience and workload to provide you with a solid foundation for the next (and more important) stage of your career as a senior house officer.

At this stage, your curriculum vitae will read just as well if you have broad experience in a busy general hospital as if you have limited experience in a more specialist centre. It is also unnecessary to think of specialising at this point – this lies several years ahead of you.

Many medical schools have some kind of 'matching system' to simplify the appointment process and avoid interminable interviews. You list which house officer jobs appeal to you and the consultants mark the students they would like as house staff. Put simply, if you impress during your student attachment then you are likely to be offered a job. As a general rule, consultants enjoy seeing their bright 'old' students developing into bright 'new' doctors! The best advice is to apply for a post on the ward you enjoyed most.

Preparation for your house officer year

The final year of medical school is a transition period from student to professional. There are several ways to help you with this transition. You should of course try to see and learn as much as possible during your attachments to the wards. Some medical schools have *'shadowing'* schemes so that future post holders can follow the current house officer to get some on-the-job experience before starting on the wards. Medical schools with this type of programme include Leicester and Manchester. Medical schools such as Newcastle and Nottingham have an intensive two-week course which deals with important aspects of the job like cardiopulmonary resuscitation and the practical prescribing of drugs, helping you to build up confidence before you start work.

Starting work

One thing that troubles junior doctors starting their first job is a fear of the unknown. Most hospitals are aware of this and arrange some kind of induction day to overcome it. This is helpful, especially if your student attachments did not include your new hospital.

You will have the opportunity to sort out important paper work (especially your bank details, so you can be paid!).

Members of the hospital medical staff will be available to take you through the hospital routine, including duty rotas, procedures for things like out-of-hours blood tests, how the bleep system works and how to call the 'crash team' to an emergency. Most hospitals provide each new doctor with a handbook of some kind as a reminder until you have got to grips with the system.

> **Hints & tips**
>
> When you start a new job, always make sure that:
>
> - Salaries and Wages have you on the payroll;
> - you know how to find the restaurant;
> - you know which ward will give you a quick coffee.

THE BLEEP SYSTEM AND THE 'CRASH BLEEP'

When you start work, you will be given a 'bleep' which allows anyone to contact you as long as the bleep is switched on. This is not good news – it means that you may be interrupted on a fairly frequent basis, irrespective of what you are doing. It is almost as if there are a range of sensors in-built to detect periods of inactivity (including sleep) and 'comfort breaks', as the Americans say. It seems your bleep just *knows* when to go off.

On selected days, you will be a member of the 'crash' or 'arrest' team. This is made up of doctors who are required to drop everything in response to medical emergencies, usually a cardiac arrest, anywhere in the hospital. You will carry a bleep which will only be activated in an emergency. The crash team will be directed to any part of the hospital to provide rapid care to anyone – patient, visiting relative or even member of staff – wherever it is needed.

This can be quite exciting, because generally running around hospital corridors is inappropriate (and sometimes dangerous) and only justified in emergencies. You will have learned CPR (cardiopulmonary resuscitation) during your training, but there is no substitute for the real thing. Your first emergency will leave you in a cold sweat – the lessons learned in medical school cannot prepare you for the speed of events. After your third or fourth, the lessons pay off, you get involved more and you help your more experienced colleagues quickly and efficiently. As your confidence and ability grow, you start thinking ahead and planning what might be needed next.

The first few weeks

Around the first week in August, newly qualified doctors all over Britain start their first job as house officers, on the bottom rung of the medical hierarchy. The year working under supervision should be an enjoyable one, a time for consolidating the lessons learned in medical school, for increasing experience and confidence, and for learning new practical skills.

The first day is a unique experience. Almost every doctor can recall a few traumas of their first day: getting lost running to a cardiac arrest; forgetting the dose of common drugs; having to deal with a bereaved family; never quite catching up with what needs to be done. As the first few weeks pass, you will learn rapidly. How to prioritise the incessant bleeps from nursing staff to see patients on various wards, how to deal with medical emergencies, how to think and act quickly and effectively. By the end of the first month, most have 'cracked it' and can cope with whatever happens. Your confidence will grow and you will begin to feel that you are making a positive contribution to the medical team.

Basic house officer duties

As a house officer, you will be expected to know as much about your patients as possible: the reasons for admission, social difficulties that indicate a potential problem when the time comes for discharge, results of tests that clinch the diagnosis, the ongoing treatment and how each patient is progressing. Your consultant, who has a legal responsibility for all patients admitted under his or her care, will of course be available to discuss problems at any time, but he or she will usually attend the ward to see all patients two days per week. This is your opportunity to shine and impress your professional colleagues, but most of all your boss.

Your consultant will expect you to present a brief history of every patient, describing what the initial symptoms were, what the diagnosis was thought to be, what tests had been done to confirm the diagnosis and how the patient was responding to treatment. Your consultant will provide advice if there are any diagnostic dilemmas or any difficulties with treatment. A well-conducted ward round will show you in a good light. A timetable of a surgical house officer's typical working week might be:.

MONDAY	*am*	Clerk patients for afternoon operating list
	pm	Assist in theatre with operating list
TUESDAY	*am*	Consultant ward round
	pm	Assist in out-patient clinic
WEDNESDAY	*am*	Minor surgery list supervised by registrar
	pm	Ward work
THURSDAY	*am*	On call – clerk emergency admissions
	pm	On call – clerk emergency admissions
FRIDAY	*am*	Consultant ward round
	pm	X-ray meeting followed by teaching seminar

If you work in a teaching hospital, or a hospital close to a medical school, you will have medical students who will be keen to watch and learn from the doctors. This now includes you, of course. It is your turn to pass on your knowledge and skills.

New doctors are usually very keen to acquire new practical skills. You will be expected to learn how to:

- provide basic and advanced life support (resuscitation);
- take blood for routine tests;
- put a cannula or tube into a vein through which drugs and fluids can be given directly into the blood stream;
- put in a urinary catheter to relieve retention of urine;
- perform a lumbar puncture, which is useful in the diagnosis of meningitis and other neurological problems;
- cannulate a large vein in the neck through which a temporary pacemaker wire can be fed into the heart.

One of the most enjoyable aspects of your job will be learning from your colleagues and becoming a useful member of a team. The doctors you work with will guide you through your first tentative weeks until you have found your feet, but will also be supportive throughout the year, offering advice and encouragement where needed.

It is a sad fact of life that funding your way through medical school is difficult and, following the Dearing report, likely to become even harder. Indeed, by the end of your final year you may find yourself financially embarrassed by a debt of several thousand pounds. The good news is that your salary as a house officer is quite good, so your debts may be repaid fairly quickly. Alternatively, spend longer paying off your bills and treat yourself to a new car and a good summer holiday. And a winter holiday as well!

'On take'

Patients who are admitted to hospital as emergencies are often looked after by a team of doctors: the house officer, senior house officer, specialist registrar and consultant who are 'on take'. In other words, it is their day to receive patients. How often this occurs and the duties you will be assigned depend upon the sort of rota system in operation locally, but typically you will be on take every fifth day, sometimes looking after emergency admissions as they arrive and at other times looking after patients who are already on the wards.

A newly admitted patient will be seen by several doctors during their hospital stay, but the house officer is often the first member of the team to see a patient. It is his or her job to make an initial assessment by enquiring about symptoms, and through examination and appropriate investigations to establish a diagnosis. This takes a lot of practice but the experience gained during your training and guidance from your colleagues means that you will learn fast.

'On take' days are usually the busiest days because the workload is somewhat unpredictable. Many of the patients you will encounter are not seriously ill, but may be too ill to be treated at home or require more specialist treatment than a general practitioner can be expected to provide. A few patients will be critically ill and will need intensive treatment for several days or even weeks.

Sudden illness is a major stress for any family, so your communication skills will be tested as anxious relatives try to come to terms with unexpected illness. You will often be bombarded with lots of questions about what the diagnosis might be, the risk to health and duration of the hospital stay. Many of these questions are premature, as a diagnosis may not be possible immediately. Even so, talking to anxious patients and relatives and being able to reassure them helps build up your confidence. You will soon learn to anticipate the questions they have and how best to handle them.

Your toughest task will be breaking bad news. This is one of the most difficult skills to master. Your lecturers will prepare you as much as they can through role play, and listening to and watching a more experienced colleague helps, but eventually you will have to face the real thing.

Mistakes

If you read newspapers at all, you might suspect that doctors spend a lot of time in court defending their reputations and their decisions. Generally speaking, patients in the UK (unlike the USA) are not particularly litigious, so most doctors will probably never face a court case. Nevertheless, a subscription to one of the medical defence societies is strongly advised, just in case!

Unfortunately, you will have to accept that what doctors do attracts media attention, not least when a doctor is accused of making a mistake or, worse, of committing a crime. You should not be anxious at this stage about the prospects of making a mistake. Your medical training will equip you with the knowledge to minimise the risks of making a wrong diagnosis and giving inappropriate treatment.

House officers are meant to be supervised in all aspects of their work and at all times; this is, of course, totally impractical and unrealistic. What actually happens in your first year is that you will see patients and make decisions which other members of the team will check. Your superiors have to bear most of the responsibility if a serious mistake is made.

Medical mistakes are of two kinds: sins of *omission* (you fail to do something you should have done) and sins of *commission* (you do something you should not have done). Obviously, neither is satisfactory. You can be reassured that mistakes are uncommon and those which are a threat to a patient's well-being even less so. The most common mistake is to prescribe the right drug but in the wrong dose. There are mechanisms to check for this, but mistakes still happen.

Patients and their relatives may complain about the care they have received. In fact you are more likely to receive a complaint from a patient for something *said* than something *done* to them. This should be a reminder to treat each patient with respect and always to do your best for every patient you meet.

The end of your house officer year

Your first year will pass quickly. Your consultants will sign a *Certificate of Competence* which verifies that you are ready to pass on to the next stage of your medical career. You have satisfied the requirements of the General Medical Council and will be rewarded with a *Certificate of Full Registration*. Its renewal each year confirms that you are licensed to continue to practise as a doctor. It is this certificate which doctors must surrender if they are 'struck off' the List of General Medical Practitioners.

The awarding of Full Registration carries with it the right to practise independently. This is somewhat optimistic, because you are still relatively inexperienced. In effect, what Full Registration means is that you are now ready for the next stage of your professional training. You will have had some thoughts already about what your career preferences might be. Perhaps you are leaning towards general practice, or to a hospital specialty such as obstetrics & gynaecology or surgery? How you choose is discussed in the next chapter.

CHAPTER TWELVE

A career in medicine

Your first year as a doctor will teach you a lot about looking after patients and working with professional colleagues (doctors, nurses and therapists), but most of all you will learn about yourself – how you are able to cope with the everyday pleasures and stresses of being a doctor. In addition, you will also begin to discover what aspects of medicine you do (and do not) find interesting and enjoyable – the first steps in planning your future career.

When they think of doctors, most people are reminded of their local GP or a high-profile doctor such as a heart surgeon. Television addicts may have heard of the forensic psychiatrist or Home Office pathologist. Few would be aware of communicable disease control or clinical immunology, despite their importance in containing outbreaks of infectious disease and in transplant work respectively.

The range of interests of those who enter medical school is enormous. A medical degree is a key to a thousand careers, some dealing with patients, some with laboratory sciences, others with research or wider issues of public health. The full list of potential careers is too long to include in full here, but a range of options is discussed below.

What influences career choice?

How can you decide which branch of medicine to follow? You may already have a good idea which area appeals to you. Indeed, one in seven doctors has decided what he or she wants to do even before they *start* medical school. This may be because of work experience, the influence of a medical member of the family, because of a popular programme on television or because they just *know* what they are cut out to be.

Enthusiasm is probably the most important reason for selecting a career pathway. Having obvious practical skills and aptitude often helps, as does an enjoyable experience of a specialty during the house officer year or as a student. If financial reward attracts you, think again – there are far easier ways to make much more money than a doctor earns, and studies confirm that a high salary does not seem a powerful influence on career choice.

The best approach is to consider each of your attachments in hospital and general practice as a potential career. During your training as a medical student, you will have direct contact with a variety of medical specialties and will become aware of many others.

It is always a good idea to accompany your patients from the wards when they go to have tests done to ascertain a diagnosis. There are two benefits to this. First, it is important that you are aware of what patients may need to go through to get a diagnosis. Second, you will gain much wider experience of medical care than if you wait for the results to be returned to the ward. For example, while you are learning about medicine, a patient may undergo sophisticated tests like CT and MRI brain scan (performed by radiologists), lumbar puncture (cells may be cultured by microbiologists), heart rhythm testing (carried out by cardiologists) and EEG or 'brain wave' analysis (carried out by neurophysiologists). Exposure to these specialties makes learning about medicine more interesting and may help you to make a career choice.

You may enter your house officer year not really knowing what you want to do. This does not matter, as you will see and learn a lot in your first few months. However, you must also give some thought to your future career, and certainly begin to consider your options seriously no later than three months into your housejob. If by this stage you really cannot decide and are wondering which senior house officer post to apply for, there are some specialties which allow you to make constructive use of your time while coming to a decision. For instance, it is probably never wrong to get some practical experience in accident & emergency. You will see a huge range of medical and surgical emergencies and this will stand you in good stead if you later opt for general practice, any branch of surgery, or indeed accident & emergency work itself. An alternative is to get some general medical experience. This time will not be wasted, as most of the health problems which delay recovery from an illness or surgery are medical ones.

You will know when the time to start applying for jobs is right, not least because your fellow house officers will suddenly take an interest in the classified section of the *British Medical Journal*, where most job vacancies are advertised. You shouldn't unduly delay in making applications: good jobs appear (and disappear) with alarming speed. If you know what you want to do, and even where you might want to apply, have your *curriculum vitae* (CV) ready to send off as soon as you spot the advertisement.

There are plenty of people who will help you with the content and design of your CV. It is worth making some effort over this as a well-presented CV may get you an interview whereas a poor one may make you fall at the first hurdle.

Which career for you?

At this stage of your life, with medical school probably still ahead of you, there is a lot to see before you have to make your mind up about what you want to do for the rest of your working life. But let us assume that you are well advanced in your medical training: how might you decide what sort of doctor you want to be?

A simple way is to look back on your undergraduate experiences and consider carefully what most appealed to you. You may have found dealing with emergencies gave you a 'buzz', but you need not constrain yourself to a hospital specialty which deals with a lot of acutely ill people. Many GPs take their own night calls and will often be first on the scene to diagnose the problem and provide emergency care, long before the patient reaches hospital.

If regular nine-to-five hours are more to your liking but you still want patient contact, psychiatry, dermatology (skin diseases), clinical genetics (diagnosing rare congenital diseases) or occupational health may be more suitable. If you are not particularly keen on dealing with patients, there are still plenty of options such as public health medicine (which focuses more on disease in communities than in individuals), environmental health or pharmaceutical medicine (advising drug companies on product design and testing) which might appeal.

Are you more interested in the science of medicine than dealing with people? If so, pathology (which helps with diagnosis from blood and tissue specimens), forensic science or academic medicine have many openings.

Some people want to become an expert in a very specialised field, for instance by training as a general surgeon and then specialising in cardiothoracic surgery – you will become particularly skilled at performing cardiac bypass surgery and putting in artificial heart valves. This is anathema to many who prefer to keep a fairly wide portfolio of skills and become a general practitioner – a doctor who requires a very broad knowledge of the entire spectrum of disease and illness, but who may also have deeper knowledge of perhaps just one area.

You need not confine your thoughts to the UK. There are opportunities to work in the developing world with Voluntary Service Overseas (VSO) or in tropical medicine.

The training you receive in medical school prepares you for the rigors of a career in any branch of medicine. Providing you keep an open mind in your training, you will soon become aware of just how broad the term *medicine* is.

Postgraduate training

It is beyond the scope of this book to consider specialty training in great detail, not least because what is currently applicable may change a great deal by the time you have to make any decisions, seven or eight years from now. Nonetheless, one aim of this book is to give you an impression of what a career in medicine involves as well as to explain some of the current 'buzz-words' that may crop up in your interview. We will therefore describe the basics of training in general practice and in a hospital specialty.

After the pre-registration house officer year come the senior house officer (SHO) years. Most doctors spend at least two years as an SHO, the exact duration often being determined by how quickly they pass postgraduate examinations such as the MRCP (for physicians), FRCS (for surgeons) and so on. For budding hospital specialists, membership of the relevant Royal College is usually a prerequisite of beginning specialist training and so they remain as SHOs until they have acquired the necessary qualifications. This period is known as *general professional training*.

Training for general practice

General practitioners have to undertake three years' vocational training in a combination of specialties and general practice itself, often packaged together as a *vocational training scheme* (or VTS). Doctors can commence vocational training after the completion of their pre-registration house officer year. The three years must include:

- one year as a trainee in general practice;
- two 'approved' training posts of at least six months' duration each (examples include obstetrics & gynaecology, paediatrics, accident & emergency and a number of others).

Any remaining time can be spent either in hospital specialties or in the community. During the training scheme, GP trainees may take additional qualifications such as the Diploma in Child Health (DCH). At the end of the training scheme, trainees may also take the examination for Membership of the Royal College of General Practitioners (MRCGP).

Training for a hospital specialty

Training for the hospital specialties underwent a major upheaval in the mid-1990s as a result of the recommendations in the report *Hospital Doctors: Training for the Future*, more widely known as the *Calman Report* (after the Chief Medical Officer, Sir Kenneth Calman). The Calman Report was, in part, a response to concern by the European Community that a two-tier system for medical training was developing across EC member states.

The Calman Report has led to the introduction of more *structured* training in the hospital specialties than before. The previous career grades of registrar and senior registrar have been replaced by a single **specialist registrar** (SpR) grade. For each hospital specialty there is now a formal training programme that lays down how long the training should take,

> **Further reading**
>
> The Calman Report is not required reading at this stage in your career. Nonetheless, if you did want to look at a copy, its reference is: *Hospital Doctors: Training for the Future. The Report of the Working Group on Specialist Medical Training (the Calman Report): Department of Health, April 1993, MISC(93)31.*

what experience (for example, in practical procedures) needs to be gained, and what assessment requirements must be met. At the satisfactory completion of training, a specialist registrar receives a *Certificate of Completion of Specialist Training* (CCST) which allows their name to be added to the Specialist Register.

Another aspect of these reforms is the introduction of **national training numbers** (NTNs). NTNs are issued to specialist registrars and allow control over the number of doctors training in a particular specialty – you can't train for your CCST without holding an NTN. By matching the number of people entering specialty training with the number of expected consultant vacancies in the future, it is hoped that everyone who trains for a consultant post in a particular specialty will be able to find one (this has not always been the case in the past).

The length of the training programme varies from specialty to specialty – in cardiology, for example, trainees are required to spend six years as a specialist registrar. This means a minimum of around nine years' training after medical school (one year as a pre-registration house officer, two years as a senior house officer, and six years as a specialist registrar) before being in a position to take up a consultant post in cardiology. Many other hospital specialties require only four or five years' experience as a specialist registrar. Some doctors may choose to spend a year or more gaining extra experience (or performing research for an MD or PhD) before starting on a specialist registrar training programme.

Part-time training

The figures quoted above for the duration of specialist registrar training assume that training is on a full-time basis. Many doctors may choose to take a career break to raise a family, or want to undertake part-time training so that they can train while bringing up small children. There is no doubt that the medical profession has been very slow to sort out reasonable part-time training programmes.

This should change, not least because of the increasing numbers of women entering the profession. Currently, women account for just over 50% of medical students but only 29% of hospital medical staff (and only 4% of consultant surgeons). The specialist registrar grade does allow some provision for flexible training. However, those applying for flexible training will have to show that *'training on a full-time basis would not be practicable for well-founded individual reasons'* (EC Directive 93/16/EEC). The decision about whether a reason is 'well-founded' is taken by the relevant postgraduate or associate dean.

Part-time training in general practice is somewhat better established. GP trainees can undertake their three years of vocational training on a part-time basis, although the training must be completed within a seven-year period.

Continuing medical education

At some time in your medical career, you will be considered 'trained' in a particular specialty and ready to take on full medical (and hence legal) responsibility for patient care. This does not mean that you will stop learning. Part of your professional responsibility is to maintain your level of knowledge, which means keeping up to date with progress in your area of expertise.

The Royal Colleges of Physicians, Surgeons and the other specialties monitor the continuing education of consultants through *continuing medical education* (CME). Consultants may attend lectures, professional meetings or specialty conferences to accumulate a sufficient number of hours of CME. The number of hours specified varies, but 50–100 hours per year is typical. It is not difficult to meet the CME requirements of the Royal Colleges; indeed, most consultants already comfortably exceed requirements through attending regular in-hospital postgraduate meetings and their annual specialty conference.

Salaries

The issue of remuneration should not play a major part in your career choices. Nonetheless, you may find it useful to have an approximate idea of what your future earnings will be, particularly when deciding whether or not to take out a student loan. We have therefore listed current (end-of-1996) salaries for the different grades of hospital doctor in table 12.1.

However, there are two things you need to bear in mind. First, it will be several years before you receive your first payslip, and the figures quoted here will certainly have changed by then. Second, the figures we have quoted are for the basic salary, not including payments for on-call work for the training grades (consultant staff do not receive additional payments for on-call work).

Table 12.1 Basic annual salaries for hospital doctors

Pre-registration house officer	£14,880
Senior house officer (year 1)	£18,560
Senior house officer (year 2)	£19,810
Specialist registrar (year 1)	£20,745
Specialist registrar (year 2)	£21,800
Specialist registrar (year 3)	£22,855
Specialist registrar (year 4)	£23,910
Specialist registrar (year 5)	£25,180
Consultant (year 1)	£42,170

At present, overtime payments depend upon the working arrangement you have when on-call. This can be a *full shift system*, a *partial shift system* or an *on-call rota*. A pre-registration house officer who is on-call one night in five would earn approximately £4800 in addition to their basic annual salary of £14,880.

Career preferences

Doctors tend to choose the following careers:

25% general practice   6% paediatrics
20% medicine   5% obstetrics & gynaecology
16% surgery   4% psychiatry
7% anaesthetics

The remaining 17% head for careers in other hospital specialties like radiology, pathology or accident & emergency, and a few for public health.

There are clear sex differences, with women more likely to choose general practice, paediatrics or obstetrics & gynaecology, and men more likely to choose surgical or medical specialties. There are several reasons for this. The hours of work, uncertainty about part-time training, about domestic and family circumstances, and well-established sex profiles in some specialties such as surgery prevail. These may change, as more women than men are now entering medical school.

General practice appears to be less popular than in the past, as only 7% of male graduates and 13% of women graduates expressed general practice as their first choice for a career, the bulk of graduates preferring a hospital-based specialty. Indeed, GP recruitment is at its lowest levels since the 1960s. The reasons for this are thought to be lack of job satisfaction and low morale in family practice and the attraction of scientific development and reduced training time in hospital specialties.

There are going to be disappointments, because for every two hospital consultants there are three GPs. Recent changes in the NHS place greater emphasis on primary care (that is, care in the community) rather than the much more expensive care in hospital. The most likely solution will be that hospital specialties will become saturated and many doctors will have to settle for their second-choice career.

Choice of medical school and future career intentions

Might your choice of medical school influence what your final career direction may be? Studies of graduates from all UK medical schools reported that certain medical schools were producing graduates who seemed to prefer to enter general practice while other schools seemed to be turning out future specialists. Later studies reported that there had been a 'sea change'. It is therefore probably fair to say that what matters most in choosing a career is the individual rather than the school. If you hear otherwise, disregard it!

Potential shortage in medical careers

It is difficult to predict how the NHS may change in the future. There are areas of medicine today where there are relative shortages of doctors. This is not new – graduates from the Indian subcontinent supported the less popular areas of medical care for years after the NHS was established. Medicine is as vulnerable to fashion as any other career. Judging from the expressed preferences of UK doctors and applications for medical posts, certain specialties, like anaesthetics and accident & emergency, appear to be increasing in popularity, and others, like general practice, pathology and psychiatry, are falling in popularity.

At this stage you should not be unduly concerned about not being able to follow the career of your choice or even of not having a job. All medical schools have access to designated housejobs, usually but not always close to the university where you will train. For example, there are 300 housejobs recognised in the Birmingham area as suitable for pre-registration training and only 180 or so Birmingham graduates, so a first job in that area is secure.

You may think you know exactly which specialty you want to train for, but at present you are at least seven years away from making that decision, and you have a lot to see and enjoy. Only 13% of doctors enter a specialty that they had considered before they went to medical school. You should aim to look forward with interest to each new specialty, and not reject any specialty until you have sampled it.

Careers in medicine

You may already have a firm idea of what you want to do after you qualify as a doctor. Even so, you will probably change your mind half a dozen times as you learn about the different aspects of each specialty. You will almost certainly not be aware of the enormous choice available to a medical graduate. In tables 12.2 and 12.3 we have listed many of the hospital and non-hospital specialties, but even these lists are by no means comprehensive.

As you progress through medical school you will come into contact with doctors from many of these specialties and see for yourself what they do. Again, it is beyond the scope of this book to describe each specialty in detail, although you may find it useful to know a little about some of the larger specialties, particularly if the topic comes up during an interview. We have therefore provided a brief description of twelve major specialties below. Information on careers in the armed forces can be found in chapter 6.

ACCIDENT & EMERGENCY

Specialists in accident & emergency ('A & E') work on the hospital's 'front door', providing immediate care for patients who present themselves to the hospital, regardless of their complaint. The work is therefore unpredictable,

Table 12.2 Hospital specialties

General (internal) medicine	Psychiatry
Cardiology	Child and adolescent psychiatry
Diabetes/endocrinology	Forensic psychiatry
Gastroenterology	Mental handicap/mental illness
Nephrology	Psychogeriatrics
Thoracic medicine	Psychotherapy
Elderly care	Pathology
Audiological medicine	Haematology
Clinical genetics	Immunology
Clinical neurophysiology	Chemical pathology/clinical chemistry
Clinical pharmacology & therapeutics	Medical microbiology
Clinical physiology	Blood transfusion
Dermatology	Histopathology
Genito-urinary medicine	Neuropathology
Medical oncology	Radiology
Infectious diseases	Diagnostic radiology
Neurology	Therapeutic radiology
Rheumatology	Radiotherapy/oncology
Paediatrics	Nuclear medicine
General surgery	Anaesthetics
Cardiothoracic surgery	Intensive care
Neurosurgery	Anaesthetics
Ophthalmology	Pain control
Otorhinolaryngology	Accident & emergency
Paediatric surgery	Obstetrics & gynaecology
Plastic surgery	Tropical medicine
Trauma & orthopaedic surgery	Rheumatology & rehabilitation
Urology	

Table 12.3 Non-hospital specialties

General practice	Clinical academic specialties
Public health/epidemiology	Armed forces
Environmental health	Occupational health
Medical journalism	Preclinical academic staff
Police surgeon	Student health
NHS management	Civil service
Pharmaceutical medicine	Medical Voluntary Service Overseas

but this is often regarded as one of its attractions – one does not know if the next patient to appear will have a sprained ankle or major injuries from a car accident. Out-of-hours commitments are relatively heavy but are normally worked on a shift system, as there is little need for continuity of care: having been assessed and given essential treatment, most patients are either discharged or passed on to other specialties for their continuing care.

ANAESTHETICS AND INTENSIVE CARE

Anaesthetists are responsible for the anaesthesia given to patients during surgical procedures. They also look after critically-ill patients on the intensive therapy unit (ITU), often requiring close monitoring with high-technology equipment. The out-of-hours commitment tends to be heavy because of the unpredictability of the emergency work.

CARDIOLOGY

Cardiologists have an interest in disorders of the cardiovascular system (the heart and blood vessels). Ischaemic heart disease (narrowing of the arteries around the heart) is a very common problem in the developed world and is responsible for much of a cardiologist's workload. Other problems seen include arrhythmias (abnormalities of the heart's rhythm) and hypertension (high blood pressure). Cardiology can be a very practical or 'hands-on' specialty, with opportunities for pacemaker implantation and cardiac catheterisation (an invasive study of the heart and arteries) among others.

GASTROENTEROLOGY

Concerned with disorders of the digestive system, gastroenterologists manage patients with conditions such as duodenal and stomach ulcers, irritable bowel syndrome and inflammatory bowel diseases. There are opportunities for practical procedures such as endoscopy (examining the inside of the digestive tract with a flexible telescope) and studies of the pancreas and bile ducts using a procedure called ERCP.

GENERAL PRACTICE

General practitioners (GPs) are concerned with the provision of *primary* health care. They are the first point of contact for most patients concerned about their symptoms. GPs assess and treat patients in the community and, when necessary, refer them to a hospital for a specialist opinion. GPs are also concerned with health *promotion* and offer various screening services (e.g. blood pressure and cholesterol checks) to try and prevent diseases before they occur. The out-of-hours commitments can be heavy.

GENERAL SURGERY

General surgeons deal with disorders that may require an operation, such as appendicitis or gallstones. There are many surgical subspecialties, including (for example):

- orthopaedic surgery (operations on the bones and joints);
- neurosurgery (operations on the brain);
- urology (operations on the bladder and, in men, the prostate gland);
- vascular surgery (operations on the blood vessels).

Surgeons have a relatively heavy out-of-hours commitment as patients requiring emergency operations can present to the hospital at any time of the day or night.

HAEMATOLOGY

Haematologists are concerned with disorders of the blood, lymph nodes and bone marrow. These include such problems as sickle-cell anaemia, haemophilia and leukaemia. As well as chemotherapy, some hospitals now offer bone-marrow transplantation for patients with leukaemia. Much of the work is laboratory-based, with responsibility for the interpretation of blood tests and bone marrow biopsies and for the provision of cross-matched blood products for transfusions.

PAEDIATRICS

Concerned with the diseases of infancy and childhood, paediatricians see patients with conditions such as congenital abnormalities (e.g. 'hole in the heart') and infectious diseases (e.g. whooping cough). Paediatricians also take responsibility for the care of critically-ill babies on the SCBU (special care baby unit) and children on the paediatric ITU (intensive therapy unit). There are opportunities to subspecialise within paediatrics, for example in paediatric cardiology.

PATHOLOGY

Pathology covers a wide range of laboratory-based specialties, including haematology (see above), clinical chemistry, immunology and microbiology. Patient contact tends to be limited in the pathological specialties, although the diagnostic services provided by the various departmental laboratories are essential for patient care. Pathologists are often consulted by their clinical colleagues for advice regarding the investigation of a patient's illness or the interpretation of an abnormal test result.

PSYCHIATRY

Psychiatrists have an interest in disorders of the mind, such as depression and schizophrenia. There are opportunities to subspecialise within such fields as forensic psychiatry or child and adolescent psychiatry. Psychiatry involves relatively light out-of-hours duties but demands the ability to communicate well with patients, often under difficult circumstances.

PUBLIC HEALTH

Specialists in public health have an interest in the health of populations rather than that of individuals. Their work includes studying the occurrence of disease within populations (epidemiology) and devising strategies for health promotion. Public health specialists may find themselves giving advice and information to local or national groups and governmental organisations to help with the planning of health care within the community.

RADIOLOGY

Radiology is a rapidly advancing and expanding specialty, with many opportunities to develop subspecialty interests. Diagnostic radiologists are concerned with the investigation of diseases by various imaging techniques, such as X-rays, CT or MRI scanning and ultrasound scanning. Those with more invasive interests can undertake angiography and angioplasty (the widening of a blood vessel with a small balloon on the tip of a catheter).

Further reading

A useful guide to career opportunities in medicine, entitled *Medical Careers – A General Guide*, is published by the British Medical Association. It is available from BMJ Bookshop, Burton Street, London WC1H 9JR
☎ (0171) 383 6185 – mail order
Members of the BMA can obtain a free copy from their local BMA office.

CHAPTER THIRTEEN

So is medicine for you?

There can be few professions where the variety of work and the range of opportunities are so broad. Medicine is a most rewarding career. There is the intellectual satisfaction of having mastered a large body of knowledge and concepts, of having specific practical and technical skills, of successfully diagnosing and treating a patient. Whichever branch of medicine might appeal to you now, within a few years you could easily find yourself with a difficult but pleasant decision: which branch of medicine is for you?

What have you got from this book?

We hope that you have found this book helpful. While your peers, friends, relatives and teachers may try to persuade you that you just *have* to apply for medicine, it has not been our intention to do anything other than to let you know what trying for a place in medical school means. We want you to know at the very least what you are letting yourself in for when you complete your UCAS form, what to expect during the course, what your early experiences will be and what avenues are open to you once you graduate.

We confess to being enthusiastic doctors. You may have felt at times as you read this book that medicine is not all it is cracked up to be, that the public image differs from the picture painted here. That too is precisely what we intended. We have deliberately tried to paint a 'warts and all' but, above all, *fair* picture of medicine. Anything less would risk deceiving you and wasting not only your time but also a valuable place on the medical course.

Whether you have read this book closely or just skimmed the pages, our main aim has been to help you decide whether medicine is right for you and whether you should make your application to medical school. If we have put you off, we make no apology – you previously must have had some reservations which we have merely confirmed. There are still lots of opportunities awaiting you, but medicine is not one of them and it is better to find out now than later. If you really are convinced that you want to become a doctor, you should by now be much more confident that you really are making a wise choice.

Motivation is the key to success. Whether you are a sixth-former about to embark on your first career, or someone who is considering a new career, you have a difficult but exciting time ahead of you. As you prepare for your A level examinations, remember that these are probably the hardest exams you will encounter. A good degree course will rely less on a good memory and more on understanding, so it is worth focusing your efforts *now* to make sure that you do your best to achieve your full potential.

Good examination grades can open the doors to a wide range of opportunities at university and subsequently to lots of careers. Unfortunately in medicine, even after a lengthy period of undergraduate training, you will only have achieved a basic qualification. You will not be considered fully trained until at least six years after you finish medical school, and two or three years more for some of the major specialties. You also need to bear in mind that the work can be mentally and physically taxing.

As a bright student, you may have had lots of advice on choosing a career. Everyone likes to see a good pupil get on and progress to a successful career. Pressure to go into a middle-class occupation like medicine may come from teachers, parents, relatives and friends alike. Eventually this may lead to acceptance that medicine is what everyone is expecting you to apply for. At this point, you should question yourself as to why *you* want to be a doctor. Question your motivation and reconsider your options if you feel that you have been pressured in any way to submit your application to medical school. Self-motivation is crucial in medical school, during the years of postgraduate training and especially when you practise as a doctor.

Thinking of taking a year out?

You may feel that after your A levels you deserve a break before you continue with your academic pursuits. A year buzzing around Europe or the USA may sound an attractive idea. Many talk about it, few actually do it. If you are tempted, do your homework and check before the interview whether the medical school looks favourably on an adventurous spirit, because attitudes to deferred entry vary widely, from the somewhat prescriptive prevalent at Nottingham (*'constructive experience expected'*), through mildly interested at Bristol (*'we are interested to know how you will spend the year'*) to totally disinterested at Manchester (*'no stipulation is made on how a year out is spent'*).

Take your pick. If you do want to travel the world, it may be better to do so before you start on the road to your career. Medicine does afford you the opportunity to travel, not least because of the salary that you may earn. There are posts in Australia and New Zealand which are similar to the UK's, and you will have an exciting time travelling back to the UK via the Far and Middle East if you take a long vacation to do so.

Maximising your chances of admission

Your immediate goal is to ensure that you are competitive in the market for an undergraduate place. If you are serious about a medical career, your single aim is to work hard to exceed or at least match the grades expected of you. Remember that, generally speaking, medical schools are not too impressed by candidates who re-present themselves after failing to make the grade the first time and expectations are raised considerably with a re-sit. This just makes it harder – as if it isn't hard enough the first time. Work hard, because in the long run it is worth a supreme effort now to ensure your place.

Help with the next edition

We hope you have enjoyed reading *Getting into Medicine* and found the advice and information useful. For our next edition, we would welcome contributions from current students (for the quotation panels) or suggestions for how we can improve the book. Please write to:

Dr Andrew R. Houghton
Getting into Medicine
c/o Hodder & Stoughton Educational
338 Euston Road
London NW1 3BH

We will acknowledge all contributions used in the next edition.

Further Reading & Information

This section lists a number of further sources of information which you can consult to supplement the information in this book.

Medical school

Learning Medicine
Written by Peter Richards, formerly Dean of St Mary's Hospital Medical School. An invaluable guide for anyone considering a career in medicine, it is updated regularly. Available from BMJ Bookshop, Burton Street, London WC1H 9JR.
☎ (0171) 383 6185 – mail order (discount available for BMA members)

Getting into Medical School
This MPW Guide by Joe Ruston can be purchased from Trotman & Co. Ltd, 12 Hill Rise, Richmond, Surrey TW10 6UA.
☎ (0181) 332 2132

How to Obtain a Place in Medical School
Written by Dr W. Graham Westall, a general practitioner. The second edition (published in 1987) can be obtained from the author at 2 St Edeyrns Road, Cardiff CF2 6TB.

A Student's Guide to Entry to Medicine
Written by Peter Richards, this guide is published by UCAS. For a copy, write to UCAS, PO Box 28, Cheltenham, Gloucestershire GL50 3SA.

Doctors To Be
Written by Susan Spindler and based upon the BBC television *Horizon* series. Available from BBC Enterprises Ltd, Woodlands, 80 Wood Lane, London W12 0TT.

Medical Education
Written by Stella Lowry, this book examines current views on medical education. It is available from BMJ Bookshop – address above (discount available for BMA members).

University application

UCAS Handbook and Application Form
For a copy, write to UCAS, PO Box 28, Cheltenham, Gloucestershire GL50 3SA. For addresses outside the UK enclose £5.00 for postage & packing.

How to Complete your UCAS Form
A book and video on the subject can be purchased from Trotman & Co. Ltd (address above).

Going to University
Available free of charge from UCAS (address above).

University and College Entrance: the Official Guide
Available from booksellers or Sheed & Ward Ltd, 14 Coopers Row, London EC3N 2BH.
☎ (0171) 702 9799

The Complete Degree Course Offers 199–
Published annually by Trotman (address above).

UK Universities Checklist
Available free of charge from UCAS (address above).

Degree Course Guides
Available from Careers Research and Advisory Centre (CRAC), Bateman Street, Cambridge CB2 1LZ. Also widely available in careers libraries.

Money matters

At the time of writing, the effects of the Dearing report (see page 107) upon student funding were still far from certain. We suggest that you contact the following agencies as required for up-to-date information:

Student funding in England and Wales
For students ordinarily resident in England and Wales information can be obtained from LEAs and from Department for Education & Employment, Publications Centre, PO Box 6927, London E3 3NZ.
☎ (0171) 510 0150   Fax (0171) 510 0196

Student funding in Scotland
For students ordinarily resident in Scotland information can be obtained from Student Awards Agency for Scotland (SAAS), Gyleview House, 3 Redheughs Rigg, South Gyle, Edinburgh EH12 9HH.
☎ (0131) 244 5887

Student funding in Northern Ireland
Information for students from Northern Ireland may be obtained from:
Department of Education for Northern Ireland, Student Support Branch,
Rathgael House, Balloo Road, Rathgael, Bangor, Co Down BT19 7PR.
☎ (01247) 279279   Fax (01247) 279100

Welsh Language Booklet
A Welsh language booklet on student funding is available from Welsh
Office Education Department, FHE1 Division, 4th Floor, Cathays Park,
Cardiff CF1 3NQ.
☎ (01222) 825831   Fax (01222) 825823

Student Loans
Information on student loans will normally be provided by your
university once you start your course, or can be obtained from Student
Loans Company Limited, 100 Bothwell Street, Glasgow G2 7JD.
☎ (0800) 40 50 10

Directory of Grant-Making Trusts
A directory giving details of 2400 grant-making organisations in Britain,
available from Charities Aid Foundation, 48 Pembury Road, Tonbridge,
Kent TN9 2JD.

NUS Information Sheets
Information sheets on student funding are published by the National
Union of Students and obtainable from NUS Publications Department,
National Union of Students, 461 Holloway Road, London N7 6LJ.

Young People's Guide to Social Security
Leaflet FB 23, available from Social Security Offices.

The armed forces

Army Medical Services
For this free booklet and further information on medical cadetships
contact: Officer Recruiting, RHQ RAMC, Keogh Barracks, Ash Vale,
Aldershot, Hants GU12 5RQ.
☎ (01252) 340307/9

Officer in the Royal Navy: Medical Officer
Obtainable free of charge from Office of Dean of Naval Medicine,
Monckton House, Institute of Naval Medicine, Alverstoke, Hants PO12
2DL.
☎ (01705) 768107   Fax (01705) 504823

Officer: Medical Officer
Obtainable free of charge from Royal Air Force, Careers Information Office, Kelvin House, Cleveiand Street, London W1P 5FB.
☎ (0171) 636 0782   Fax (0171) 436 1707

Taking a year out

A Year Off . . . or a Year On?
Details of work experience and voluntary service available. Obtainable from Careers Research and Advisory Centre (address above).

Taking a Year Out: Making the most of your gap year
A comprehensive source of information and ideas, written by Polly Bird, published by Hodder & Stoughton Educational and available from bookshops.

Mature students

University Entrance: Mature Students
Available free of charge from UCAS (address above).

Stepping Up: A Mature Student's Guide to Higher Education
Free leaflet which gives information on preparing for a degree course, funding and fees, application procedures and formal qualifications. Available from UCAS (address above).

Returning to Learning
This Longman Students' Guide, written for mature students by Ted Wragg and Allen Parrott, is available from bookshops.

Overseas students

Higher Education in the United Kingdom. A Handbook for Students from Overseas and their Advisers
Published every two years for the Association of Commonwealth Universities and the British Council. Available from Longman Group Ltd, 6th Floor, Westgate House, The High, Harlow, Essex CM20 1NE.

The British Council's Guide to Studying and Living in Britain
Available from Northcote House Publishers Ltd, Plymbridge House, Estover Road, Plymouth, Devon PL6 7PZ. Copies may also be consulted at local British Council offices.

Study abroad
Published by UNESCO and obtainable from The Stationery Office, PO Box 276, London SW8 5DT.

Financial Aid for First Degree Study at Commonwealth Universities
Details of awards, almost all of which are for students from developing countries. Published by Association of Commonwealth Universities, 36 Gordon Square, London WC1H 0PF.

Studying in Scotland

Entrance Guide to Higher Education in Scotland
For details of where obtainable, contact The Secretary, COSHEP, 141 West Nile Street, Glasgow G1 2PN.
☎ (0141) 353 1880

Internet resources

All the universities and/or medical schools listed in chapter 3 have a home page on the World Wide Web and we have included the appropriate WWW address with each entry.

There are also some sites of more general interest to prospective medical students. One of these is the **Interactive Medical Student Lounge**, which can be found at:
　　http://falcon.cc.ukans.edu/~nsween/

The majority of material at this site has a strong United States emphasis, but there is some information of interest to UK medical school applicants. The same is also true of **Brad's Premed Resource Center**, which can be found at:
　　http://rio.atlantic.net/~xyz/premed.html

Also available on the World Wide Web is **The Journal of Pre-Med Studies**, produced in New York and containing material of general interest for medical school applicants:
　　http://magic.hofstra.edu:7003/premed/pre_med.html

A **Newsgroup** caters for those with an interest in medical education, and can be found at:
　　misc.education.medical

An increasing number of newspapers are also making some or all of their contents available via the Internet. At **The Times** site you can search for

stories on particular subjects, such as 'medicine' or 'NHS', which can be useful in preparation for an interview:
http://www.the-times.co.uk/

You can also find material from **The Daily Telegraph** at:
http://www.telegraph.co.uk/

The British Medical Association produces a special version of its journal, the BMJ, for medical students. An index to extracts from the **Student BMJ** can be found at:
http://www.bmj.com/bmj/studbmj/index.html

Tomorrow's Doctors

This appendix contains the principal recommendations of the Education Committee of the General Medical Council, as listed on page 23 of their report entitled *Tomorrow's Doctors*, published in December 1993. The recommendations are reproduced here with the permission of the General Medical Council.

Principal recommendations

1. The **burden of factual information** imposed on students in undergraduate medical curricula should be substantially reduced.

2. **Learning** through curiosity, the exploration of knowledge, and the critical evaluation of evidence should be promoted and should ensure a capacity for self-education; the undergraduate course should be seen as the first stage in the continuum of medical education that extends throughout professional life.

3. **Attitudes** of mind and of behaviour that befit a doctor should be inculcated, and should imbue the new graduate with attributes appropriate to his/her future responsibilities to patients, colleagues and society in general.

4. The **essential skills** required by the graduate at the beginning of the pre-registration year must be acquired under supervision, and proficiency in these skills must be rigorously assessed.

5. A **'core curriculum'** encompassing the essential knowledge and skills and the appropriate attitudes to be acquired at the time of graduation should be defined.

6. The 'core curriculum' should be augmented by a series of **'special study modules'** which allow students to study in depth areas of particular interest to them, that provide them with insights into scientific method and the discipline of research, and that engender an approach to medicine that is questioning and self-critical.

7. The 'core curriculum' should be **system-based**, its component parts being the combined responsibility of basic scientists and clinicians **integrating** their contributions to a common purpose, thus eliminating the rigid pre-clinical/clinical divide and the exclusive departmentally-based course.

8. There should be emphasis throughout the course on **communication skills** and the other essentials of basic clinical method.

9. The theme of **public health medicine** should figure prominently in the curriculum, encompassing health promotion and illness prevention, assessment and targeting of population needs, and awareness of environmental and social factors in disease.

10. Clinical teaching should adapt to **changing patterns in health care** and should provide experience of primary care and of community medical services as well as of hospital-based services.

11. **Learning systems** should be informed by modern educational theory and should draw on the wide range of technological resources available; medical schools should be prepared to share these resources to their mutual advantage.

12. **Systems of assessment** should be adapted to the new-style curriculum, should encourage appropriate learning skills and should reduce emphasis on the uncritical acquisition of facts.

13. The design, implementation and continuing review of curricula demand the establishment of effective **supervisory structures** with interdisciplinary membership and adequate representation of junior staff and students.

14. The Education Committee of the General Medical Council should ensure the **implementation of its recommendations** through regular progress reports from medical schools, continuing dialogue on the basis of informal visits and, when necessary, by the exercise of the statutory powers given to it under the Medical Acts.

Prospectus requests

The contact address provided for each medical school in chapter 3 should normally be used only for specific enquiries about the course or your application for it. Straightforward requests for a copy of the university prospectus should be sent to the addresses listed in this appendix.

Send prospectus requests on a postcard, remembering to include:
- your name and address;
- your proposed year of entry;
- the name of the course you are interested in.

A number of medical schools produce an additional, more detailed, booklet to supplement the information contained in the general university prospectus. If you state you are interested in the medical course you will usually find that a copy, or details of how to request one, is sent to you with the general prospectus.

Keep prospectus requests short and to the point. A suggested format is:

Dear Sir/Madam
Please send a copy of your undergraduate prospectus, together with details of the MB BS course in medicine, to me at the following address. I would intend to start the course in October 199–.

My address is: Alex Smith
                  1 High Street
                  Anytown
                  ANYSHIRE AB1 2CD

Thank you for your help

Yours faithfully
(Signature)

University of Aberdeen
Admissions Office, The University of
Aberdeen, Aberdeen AB9 1FX
☎ (0122) 427 3504

University of Birmingham
The Admissions Secretary, The
University of Birmingham, Edgbaston,
Birmingham B15 2TT
☎ (0121) 414 3344

University of Bristol
The Undergraduate Admissions Office,
The University, Bristol BS8 1TH
☎ (0117) 928 9000

University of Cambridge
Cambridge Intercollegiate
Applications Office (CIAO), The Old
Schools, Cambridge CB2 1TT
☎ (01223) 337733

University of Dundee
The Admissions Office, The University,
Dundee DD1 4HN
☎ (01382) 344028

University of Edinburgh
The Admissions Office, The University,
Edinburgh EH8 9YL
☎ (0131) 650 1000

University of Glasgow
The Assistant Registrar (Admissions),
The University, Glasgow G12 8QQ
☎ (0141) 330 4575

University of Leeds
The Access Office, The University,
Leeds LS2 9JT
☎ (0113) 233 2332

University of Leicester
Admissions Officer, University of
Leicester, University Road, Leicester
LE1 7RH
☎ (0116) 252 2522

University of Liverpool
Medical Admissions Tutor, PO Box
147, Liverpool L69 3BX
☎ (0151) 794 2000

University of London
*King's College School of Medicine
and Dentistry*
The Admissions Co-ordinator
(Medicine), King's College School of
Medicine and Dentistry, Bessemer
Road, London SE5 9PJ
☎ (0171) 737 4000 ext. 4017

Imperial College School of Medicine
School of Medicine Admissions,
Imperial College, London SW7 2AZ
☎ (0171) 594 3598

*Royal Free Hospital School of
Medicine*
Medical School Registry, Royal Free
Hospital School of Medicine, Rowland
Hill Street, London NW3 2PF
☎ (0171) 830 2686

*St Bartholomew's and the Royal
London School of Medicine and
Dentistry*
Admissions Office, St Bartholomew's
and the Royal London School of
Medicine and Dentistry, Queen Mary
and Westfield College, Mile End Road,
London E1 4NS
☎ (0171) 975 5555

St George's Hospital Medical School
Admissions Officer, St George's
Hospital Medical School, Cranmer
Terrace, London SW17 0RE
☎ (0181) 725 5992

*United Medical and Dental Schools
of Guy's and St Thomas's Hospitals*
Admissions Officer, United Medical
and Dental Schools of Guy's and St
Thomas's Hospitals, Lambeth Palace
Road, London SE1 7EH
☎ (0171) 922 8013

University College London Medical School
The Registrar, University College London Medical School, Gower Street, London WC1E 6BT
☎ (0171) 387 7050

University of Manchester
University Admissions Office, University of Manchester, Manchester M13 9PL
☎ (0161) 275 2065

University of Newcastle
Admissions Officer, University of Newcastle upon Tyne, Newcastle upon Tyne NE1 7RU
☎ (0191) 222 6138/8672

University of Nottingham
Admissions Office, The University of Nottingham, University Park, Nottingham NG7 2RD
☎ (0115) 951 5151

University of Oxford
The Secretary, Colleges Admissions Office, University Offices, Wellington Square, Oxford OX1 2JD
☎ (01865) 270207

The Queen's University of Belfast
The Admissions Office, The Queen's University of Belfast, University Road, Belfast BT7 1NN
☎ (01232) 245133 ext. 3081

University of Sheffield
Undergraduate Admissions Office, The University of Sheffield, Sheffield S10 2TN
☎ (0114) 276 6222

University of Southampton
Admissions Office, The University of Southampton, Southampton SO17 1BJ
☎ (01703) 595000

University of St Andrews
Director of Admissions, The University of St Andrews, College Gate, St Andrews KY16 9AJ
☎ (01334) 462150/462151/462152

University of Wales
Admissions Officer, University of Wales, PO Box 494, Cardiff CF1 3YL
☎ (01222) 874899